The Study of Kiryo

Awakening the Symbiotic Healing Power

Tadashi Kanzawa

Translated by Nimish Pratha

Book Illustrations: Miho Fukumoto

Prepared for publication by James Van Gelder

Editing Assistance: Winston Wall

This is an English translation of the Japanese version originally published in 2013:

KIRYO-KOZA by Tadashi Kanzawa

（『気療講座』 神沢 瑞至 著）

Copyright © Tadashi Kanzawa 2013

All rights reserved.

Original Japanese edition published by BUNGEISHA CO., LTD, Tokyo.

This English edition published by arrangement with BUNGEISHA CO., LTD., Tokyo

in care of Tuttle-Mori Agency, Inc., Tokyo

ISBN-13: 978-0996192927   ISBN-10: 0996192921

First published in USA by Wheel of Knowledge Publishing in 2018
Copyright © 2018 by James Van Gelder

www.WheelofKnowledge.org

Note from the Translator

Belief in an energy that suffuses all of creation is one of humanity's oldest. Much of religious thought holds that man is connected to a universal animus. It is from this animus that man is created, and into this animus that he returns. In Hinduism, this animus is called Brahman. Man's oldest medical practices also reference this pervasive spirit and seek to characterize and modify its flow through the human body to alleviate illness and bring about well-being. Ancient Indian Ayurvedic medicine classifies people into categories based on the nature of their spirit, and tailors its treatments accordingly. As someone of Asian Indian ancestry, I was raised around these ideas.

Kiryo, then, is not entirely without precedent in the history of human thought. Nor were its principles unfamiliar to me when I first learned of them. It is, however, unique among the disciplines that precede it, and those with which my upbringing acquainted me, in that it does not dance around or attempt to stand apart from accepted scientific fact. Kanzawa makes a sincere effort to ground his theories in scientific rigor. And though he makes no claim at being either a scientist or a doctor, much of his ideas match what scientists and doctors are just beginning to discover.

Biological and anthropological investigation into the evolution of modern man confirms Kanzawa's story of the development of the cerebrum, and the attendant shrinking of the brainstem. We know that part of what enabled our ancestors to form the complex societies that laid the foundation for civilization was a shrinking of the so-called "primal brain": parts of the brain that perpetuate our most animalistic qualities. As our primal brain shrunk, or perhaps because it did, our outer brain, our cerebral cortex, grew larger, enabling us to control our emotive flights with composed, logical thought. The specific neural effects of this most recent period of man's evolution are at the very frontier of modern study of anthropogeny. And yet, these are all processes that Kanzawa himself discusses.

In a way, then, Kanzawa's ideas are quite well-timed, if not somewhat prescient. And as Kanzawa himself discusses, they meet a societal need that only grows more pressing with each passing year. Many of the problems discussed by Kanzawa as plaguing Japanese society apply to American society, as well. Doctors in the West are becoming increasingly aware of a need to modify standard treatment practices to better combat diseases that do not arise from or spread via the principles medicine was built upon.

Much of the foundational work of medicine—work that shaped the mores and traditions of the profession and continues to shape its practice in the modern age—was done in battle with infectious disease. Diseases like tuberculosis and cholera, like smallpox and influenza. And through the insightful brilliance and tireless labor of countless physicians and researchers, we have largely conquered infectious disease. Now a new beast raises its head, and some would say we are ill-equipped to meet it on the plains. Psychological and psychosomatic illnesses—what Kanzawa refers to as "lifestyle diseases"—are on the rise, both because we have become better at detecting their insidious presence and because the trappings of our age may even exacerbate their symptoms. Alternative, integrative approaches to the maintenance of well-being will be pivotal in ensuring the health of our communities and those of our children. I believe that what Kanzawa has developed under the banner of Kiryo can help. I myself suffered for much of my adolescence from severe chronic illness and found significant solace in energy work similar to what Kanzawa describes herein.

Translating this book, then, has been an incredibly meaningful experience for me. And while the journey was not always easy—I grappled, just as Kanzawa once did, with how to verbalize concepts that had never before been expressed in this language—it certainly was rewarding. I am indebted to James and everyone else at Wheel of Knowledge; I am grateful to have been given the chance to contribute, in whatever small way I can, to the distribution of health-focused practice and knowledge throughout the world. I truly hope you, the reader, may find something of meaning in these pages. Thank you for picking them up.

Nimish K. Pratha

February 12, 2018

University of California, San Diego

La Jolla, California

Note from the Author

Japanese society is rushing headlong into a historically unprecedented period of extended lifespans for its population. Up until the modern era, it was common to say, "a life of fifty years." However, nowadays, the phrase, "a life of eighty years," has become commonplace.

What does this thirty-year gap signify? The fight against old age and illness. Japan's population has shifted towards a decline. With a low birth-rate and the increasing lifespans, it is estimated that the demographic percentage of elderly citizens will become extremely high in the future.

With old age comes increased reports of illness and injury. Therefore, the average bodily strength of the Japanese population will fall as an overall metric. When physical well-being declines, a country's economic power also follows it into decline. Further, the level of burden that the aging generation places on the younger generation that supports it also increases. It seems that we should do whatever we can to avoid putting a higher burden on our young generation due to the apparently rising trend of elderly inhabitants, and the related growths of sickness and injury.

It is estimated that in the future, one in every two people will get cancer, and one in three will die of it. Until recently, these facts were unimaginable. In response to this substantial predicted change in the number of cancer and lifestyle diseases, Japan put the Health Promotion Act into law. Kiryo can be adapted to suit the aim of the Health Promotion Act and correct this problem.

Kiryo has three core ideas.

The first is self-help. Self-help refers to the fact that one can protect one's own health. Self-help improves the self-healing power and has the potential to heal one's injuries and illnesses.

The second is reciprocal help. Reciprocal help allows us to use the other-healing power to heal the illnesses and injuries of both ourselves and another.

The third is self-control. Self-control is the willingness to give oneself over entirely to the sensory world. The sensory world does not depend on the inventive devices of cognitive activity. It is a world of "feeling as you are", "being as you are": a world where everything is entrusted to the brainstem.

These three ideas are the fundamentals of this book's Kiryo theory, and the aim of Kiryo. These three ideas seek out the vague, vast, and limitless world of 'Ki' inside the body. Kiryo focuses on the body's nervous functions, and it is in these nervous functions that the Kiryo effects can be found. Put simply, in Kiryo the fundamental belief is that if nervous function becomes good and proper, then one's health will be promoted.

The purpose of Kiryo theory is to enable normal people to gain an understanding of a new concept that can help them recover from illness and/or injury. In fact, the purpose of Kiryo theory is to help people to achieve an understanding of self and other healing powers to understand and control the basic nature of healing itself.

Resources lie beneath the soil of this Earth, and scientific advancements have allowed humans to use these underground resources. This has contributed to the progress and development of humanity. Similarly, inside our bodies, the health resources of the self and other healing powers have lied dormant, yet their tremendous gifts remain accessible for us.

At present, science and medicine are quite advanced, and we are in an age of regenerative medicine made possible by biotechnology. However, despite these advances in regenerative medicine, I would urge others to use these modern technologies to the minimum extent and only when necessary as our internal health resources can be effectively activated immediately.

The world we live in has changed drastically, though more recently, natural methods are being supplemented as alternative care, especially in areas where modern medical treatment methods are not sufficient. By applying the untapped health resources within our bodies, Kiryo, as an alternative, supplementary treatment, can greatly contribute to helping our bodies restore and recover themselves from illness and injury. This also contributes to controlling the costs of healthcare and treatment.

Furthermore, if we use our naturally imbued health resources to their fullest extent, the aging nation of Japan can break away from being sick and instead become healthy. The Kiryo theory put forth in this book comes from a burning desire to contribute to the health promotion of Japan.

Finally, upon the occasion of the publication of this book, I reserve special thanks to President Tsunanobi Uritani of Bungeisha, Ms. Atsuko Fujii of Tama Salon, and Mr. Kiyotaka Takahashi of the editing department. Thank you all so much.

Tadashi Kanzawa

Kiryo Academy Director

January 2013

Healing and Treatment

Attitudes Towards Illness and Injury Regarding "healing" and "treatment"

I would like to look at the meanings of the words "healing" and "treatment" from the perspective of *Kiryo*.

"Healing" refers to the process by which illnesses and injuries naturally heal from within the body. Within our bodies, there are physiological functions that exterminate sickness and injury from the inside and thus protect our life. We refer to these collectively as the *life defense system*. Our bodies are equipped with a healing power that allows them to, on their own, recover from illness and injury.

On the other hand, "treatment" is used when referring to the curing of illnesses and injuries. Additionally, it refers to the external application of various measures or procedures to the body to proactively try to cure it from injury or sickness. Our cognitive functions prompt us to attempt to cure illnesses and injuries by responding to symptoms with some type of medical treatment.

The fact that modern medical science and Eastern medicine are the main players in treatment is widely known. In these practices, therapies are primarily physical, however there are also therapies of a more spiritual basis. For example, where one hopes for perfect health or prays that their injuries and illnesses vanish. It is perhaps best to say that "treatment" refers to external application of physical or spiritual techniques to heal the body of its illnesses and injuries.

The Relationship Between Healing and Treatment

As healing involves recovery from injury or illness from the inside, it is generally a passive concept. On the contrary, treatment is the healing of illness or injury from the outside, and so is generally deemed as active. These definitions will help us to have a better understanding of these two forms of healing.

When we consider these two concepts, we see that, according to recent trends, the drive to immediately go off to treat illness and injury is very strong in modern society. Of course, I do not seek to advise anyone to deny medical treatment, I'm merely stating that the amount of people who believe that treatment alone can be used as a means to cure illness and injury continues to increase.

However, is it not ultimately because of one's own healing power—that is, the healing power one innately possesses—that one is recovered and restored from illnesses and injuries? Treatment is, at the end of the day, merely a means of stimulating such recovery and restoration.

Though external treatment assists in recovering and restoring one from illness and injury, internal healing power recovers and restores illness and injury from within. To put it another way, we may say that while treatment is a means, internal healing is the essential centerpiece of recovery and restoration.

Now, let us investigate the history of how healing and treatment are connected to the cerebrum and brainstem.

Healing is Centered Around the Brainstem

In prehistoric times, it was believed that our ancestors' cerebra were still developing (primitive cerebrum), and as such, their cognitive abilities were weak, and the physiological activities found in the brainstem were centrally dominant. The so-called "primitive brainstem" developed in a harsh natural environment and competed in a survival-of-the-fittest war for existence. When injury or illness arose, because medical treatments like those we have today did not exist, these could only have been healed with internal healing—that is, the life defense system centered around the primitive brainstem.

With this innate healing power illness and injury was able to be overcome by those who were capable of utilizing it in order to rise through the harsh conditions of natural selection. Following this line of reasoning, is it not thanks to this primitive healing power that we modern humans exist? The brainstem handles essential functions that keep us alive. In other words, battles with illness are fought with the activity of the brainstem. Therefore, the brainstem function is labeled as the source of healing power. We modern humans use this healing power unconsciously even today, as we fight to not fall ill.

However, we now, more than ever, lead our lives through the use of cognitive (linguistic) activities centered around the cerebrum, and as such, it is important to discuss the relationship between the cerebrum and the brainstem.

Treatment is Centered Around the Cerebrum

Our ancestors, who survived thanks to the activities (physiological functions) centered around the brainstem, eventually achieved, over many years, the development and evolution of the cerebrum. It is thought that through this developmental and evolutionary process, the cerebrum and brainstem were repeatedly stimulated and suppressed, respectively, as part of a feedback system.

Whilst repeating this process of stimulation and suppression, the cerebrum enlarged, eventually becoming the size it is in humans today. As this process continued over time, the cerebrum acquired two functions.

The first is *intellectual function*. This capacity, with special regards to linguistic activity, has allowed modern humans to build a civilized society. However, in order for us to be able to exercise the capacities of this intellectual function, it was necessary for the cerebrum to exercise a certain measure of control on the brainstem.

In other words, it is thought that in order to harmonize the feral, wild activity of the primitive brainstem with the cerebrum, the cerebrum needed to develop a suppressive function; this is the cerebral suppressive function that is exercised upon the brainstem. Cerebral inhibition of the brainstem is what enabled us to develop linguistic activity.

Many things were born from advancement in intellectual function, from the adoration of nature in songs or poems, to the adoration of God and religion. In due time, philosophy, too, was born. After that, on the basis of philosophy, modern medicine and various other medical disciplines were born.

The cognitive activity of the cerebrum (linguistic activity) gave rise to the treatment methods that we know of today to cure illness and injury. It gave rise to treatment methods that originate from the capacities of the cerebrum. In particular, Western medicine's conquering of infectious diseases is one of Western medicine's most storied achievements. As another example, IPS cells[1] (induced pluripotent stem cells) have captured attention at the cutting edge of medical science for their treatment potential, showing that we humans have developed yet another treatment method to stand against the harsh world of natural selection via the capacities of our cerebrum.

Humanity's primitive cerebrum and brainstem developed and evolved into the modern cerebrum and brainstem that it has today. It is through the work of this suppressive function that we have come from the irrationality and impulsiveness of the primitive brainstem to the modern brainstem we have today, that lives in a cultured society made possible by the advancements of medicine and science. It can be said that our brainstems, while maintaining harmony (suppression) with our cerebra, became modern brainstems.

In our modern brains, there is an inherent disposition to accumulate and remember the occurrences of past events. Consequently, it is very possible that memories passed down unbroken from prehistoric times have accumulated as genetic information in our cerebra. And just as this is possible for the cerebrum, so too is it possible that, in our modern brainstems, physiological functions passed down unbroken from primitive times may have accumulated as genetic information. In other words, the primitive brainstem, as genetic information, may lie deeply asleep inside the modern brainstem.

This means that the primitive brainstem, due to the suppressive function of the cerebrum, has been sealed away inside the modern brainstem and is in a deep latent sleep in the form of the genetic information of physiological memory.

Why is there such a difference between the healing power of the primitive brainstem of our primordial era and the healing power of the modern brainstem of today's world?

It is not difficult to imagine that the healing power of the primitive brainstem, which existed in a very harsh natural environment, was far more capable than our brainstem today.

---

[1] Induced pluripotent stem cells are cells that can be "induced" into forming any cell type. Most normal cells can only be one type; IPS cells can be changed into any type, showing great promise for regenerative medicine.

So, what happened to the healing power of our brainstem?

The healing power of the brainstem is what is commonly referred to today as *natural healing power*. Though not as fluently and effortlessly capable as it once was, the symbiotic healing power of the primitive brainstem still lies latently dormant as genetic information inside the modern brainstem and can be accessed, strengthened, and expanded upon.

Towards an Age Where the Symbiotic Healing Power of the Primitive Brainstem Is Used

As a fundamental conclusion of Kiryo theory, I have elected to refer to the healing power of the primitive brainstem, lying dormant as genetic information inside the modern brainstem, as *symbiotic healing power*.

At this point, there is one thing we should be aware of: it is impossible to logically develop an explanation of Kiryo based on the generally accepted concepts of Ki or Ki energy. It is impossible to specifically explain, using the concepts of Ki or Ki energy, how the healing from illness and injury that occurs during Kiryo exercise and Kiryo healing comes about. When bound to the vague, limitless world of Ki, investigating the true nature of Kiryo is difficult.

Why we actually recover and restore ourselves from illness and injury is, in truth, nearly impossible to explain. Therefore, in this book, by considering the healing sensory functions as a set of physiological functions I have sought to explain the true nature of Kiryo: the symbiotic healing power of the primitive brainstem.

Kiryo theory confidently states that the corporal (bodily) healing effects which occur when Kiryo healing and Kiryo exercises are performed provide a phenomenological illumination of the true nature of Kiryo itself. In other words, by switching the cornerstone of Kiryo theory from Ki to the *symbiotic healing power*, many doubts and questions regarding Kiryo can be resolved.

Also, it's found that under the umbrella of healing, there actually exist two different forms of healing power. They are the natural healing power of the modern brainstem, and the symbiotic healing power of the primitive brainstem (the self- and other-healing power).[2]

Just as natural resources sleep within the soil of this earth, so too does the symbiotic healing power, a healing resource, sleep within us. With the tools of Kiryo exercise and Kiryo healing, and through the application of the principles of feeling and being as you are, the symbiotic healing power can be unearthed and awakened.

Using the symbiotic force allows one to recover and restore themselves from illness and injury. Future illnesses can also be prevented. In Kiryo, there is no theoretical or practical conception of the idea of "treatment." This is because the symbiotic healing power that is within the body can ultimately cause illnesses and injuries to heal themselves. Further, using the symbiotic healing power, the healthy years of the Japanese people can be extended: health promotion can be achieved.

---

[2] Note from the translator: Kanzawa doesn't elaborate very much on this capability, but he explains that the reason one's wounds, etc., heal even if they haven't awakened their symbiotic healing power is because the modern brainstem retains a small natural healing power that can slowly heal things. See Page 25 for a clear mention of this natural healing power.

Table of Contents

Note from the Translator iii

Note from the Author.. v

Healing and Treatment... viii

    The Relationship Between Healing and Treatment................................ viii

    Towards an Age Where the Symbiotic Healing Power of the Primitive
    Brainstem Is Used.. xii

Table of Contents... xiv

Prologue: From Body-External Ki to Body-Internal Symbiotic Healing
Power 1

Chapter 1: The Healing Sensory Function   Forgotten by Humans....... 5

    1. Classifying Ki into Two General Categories 5

    2. The History of the Brainstem and the History of the Cerebrum.......... 9

Chapter 2: Kiryo Focuses on the Activity of the Nerves............................... 14

    1. Searching for the Origin of Sensory Healing:... 14

    2. Kiryo is the Origin of Healing... 23

Chapter 3: Awaken Your Primitive Brainstem 28

    Physiology from the Perspective of Kiryo 28

    2. Discovering the Activity and Role of the Kiryo Nerves....................... 30

    3. The Activity and Role of the Perceptive   Differentiation
    Nerve 33

    4. The Activity and Role of the Sensory Stiffening Nerve 39

    5. The Unified Effects of the Kiryo Nervous System and the Modern
    Medical Nervous System 50

Chapter 4: Kiryo Exercise   (Mastery of the
Symbiotic Healing Power):   Neurotransmissive Exchange 86

    1. The Goal of Kiryo Exercise is Mastery of the Symbiotic Healing
    Power 86

    2. Things to Keep in Mind When Doing Kiryo   Exercise............... 87

    3. Neurotransmissive Exchange Occurs Even in Solo Kiryo Exercise... 90

    4. Kiryo Exercise: Mastery of the Symbiotic Healing Power 98

    5. Two-Person Kiryo Exercise 109

6. Large Group Kiryo Exercise (Symbiotic Healing Power Mastery) ...115

7. Kiryo Self-Healing (Recovery and Restoration 116

of Illness and Injury) 116

Chapter 5: Kiryo Partner-Healing 122

   1.   Two Life-Energies 122

2. Kiryo Partner-Healing 124

3. Kiryo Healing for Pets 147

4. Summary of Kiryo Theory 158

Chapter 6: A Wholesome (Healthy) Brainstem as a Result of Kiryo 167

1. Kiryo and Scientific Experimentation: The Television Broadcast 167

2. A Wholesome Brainstem as an Effect of Kiryo 176

Afterword 186

Health Promotion Act 189

Glossary 190

Author Timeline 196

Prologue: From Body-External Ki to Body-Internal Symbiotic Healing Power

It has long been said in Kiryo that *Ki exists everywhere*, that *Ki is possessed by all people*, and that *it involves becoming a medium for natural energy*. These ideas have been fundamental in Kiryo for some time.

However, the extreme difficulty of scientifically defining Ki or Ki energy troubled me for many years. This was partially because there existed absolutely no phrase in the Japanese language for a variation of Ki that heals illness and injury.

The "Ki" character (気) that is used in many expressions in Japanese such as "take care," "be healthy," and the like, has now come to be used across a variety of disciplines and in various contexts, from the conversational to the academic. However, in ancient times, if one were to believe that illnesses and injuries could heal due to an invisible force, and there were no words for it, the entire phenomenon was treated with a sense of reverence and mystery, or as some sort of supernatural ability.

People were unable to verbalize this phenomenon of an invisible power healing illnesses and injuries. We lacked the terminology to define, and therefore control, a Ki that can heal illnesses and injuries. This is true even today.

Eventually, in 1972, diplomatic relations between China and Japan were established, exchange began, and Chinese *Qigong* reentered Japan after splitting apart long ago [the "Qi" in Qigong is written identically to Ki; almost insisting upon a common ancestor at some time in the ancient past].

I would think that to us Japanese, who, at that time, had little concept of a Ki that could heal illness and injury, the world of Chinese Qigong may

1

have seemed somewhat strange, mysterious, or even shocking. In truth, I also probably thought the same of the world of Kiryo until my eyes were opened to it.

Chinese Qigong is based on the following: receiving energy from the universe into the body; heightening this energy; using this energy to heal one's mind and body; and using this energy to heal others as well. In other words, Chinese Qigong believes in seeking and manipulating Ki from outside the body along with viewing Ki/Qi as the energy of the universe.

After awakening to Kiryo, and due to the influence of Chinese Qigong, I made the idea of becoming a medium for natural energy fundamental to the practice of Kiryo. That is, I sought to harness the natural energy of Ki from outside of the body. Knowing absolutely nothing of Ki at the time, I couldn't help but be influenced by the ideas of Chinese Qigong.

Since I was awakened to Kiryo, I'd always noticed that I felt a cool, blowing feeling on my palms. Thus, while developing the idea of becoming a medium for natural energy—that is, a body-external Ki— a core tenet of Kiryo, I continued to hold a simple question in my heart: *What exactly is that cool, blowing feeling?* I eventually came to question whether this sensation was produced by a certain activity of the sensory stiffening nerve. This spurred me to focus my investigations on nervous activity. This eventually led me to understand the existence of the physiological function forgotten by us humans: the *healing sensory function.*

Kiryo theory establishes that the healing sensory function is a form of nervous activity. In modern medical science, nervous activity is already common knowledge. However, from the perspective of Kiryo, we have come to realize that there are many forms of nervous activity that can be explained through the investigation of Kiryo phenomenology. Furthermore, it can be seen through such investigations that the reason illnesses and injuries are restored is because of healing nervous activity.

This healing nervous system, that is to say, the activity of the Kiryo nervous system, is, in reality, lying dormant and primarily unused due to the suppressive function of the cerebrum. This Kiryo nervous system consists of the *primitive brainstem*, the *Kiryo nerve*, the *perceptive differentiation nerve*, and the *sensory stiffening nerve*.

The Kiryo nerve is similar to the cranial nerves and the spinal nerves; it can be considered the *healing force nerve*. The perceptive differentiation nerve

2

perceives and differentiates the strength or weakness and quality of life-energy. The sensory stiffening nerve, after being stimulated by life energy, causes instantaneous stiffening contraction and relaxation in the muscles: making them softer.

The Kiryo nervous system itself, centered around the primitive brainstem, is largely unused. Through the "feeling as you are" process of Kiryo exercise and Kiryo healing, the suppressive function of the cerebrum is mitigated, and the Kiryo nervous system can be reactivated.

Reactivation of the Kiryo nervous system causes dormant Kiryo life energy to be released inside the body. We possess within ourselves a healing power that allows illnesses and injuries to recover naturally. In Kiryo, when Kiryo life energy is produced internally, the symbiotic healing power that proactively heals illnesses and injuries is actualized.

Now then, if one were to ask the method of awakening this symbiotic healing power, I would respond that there is but one: the performance of Kiryo exercise or Kiryo healing in the "feel as you are" state. When Kiryo exercise and Kiryo healing begins, the Kiryo nervous system is activated, Kiryo life energy is produced inside the body, and the symbiotic healing power is actualized.

In Kiryo exercise, Kiryo life energy produced inside the body is released through the palm of the practitioner's hand as they form the *ku-no-ji palm* with all five fingers of their hand. The ku no ji palm is performed by shaping the hand into a cupped shape, as if catching water in the palm of one's hand.[3] The energy released from the ku no ji is melded with that of one's partner. In essence, Kiryo exercise is the practice of working with a partner to mutually draw out and heighten each other's Kiryo life energy through the palm via the ku no ji hand. The ku-no-ji shape can effectively be made with the sole of one's foot as well, just as is done with the hand.

Heightening one's Kiryo energy allows one to elevate and eventually master the symbiotic healing power. As for Kiryo exercise, because it heightens this symbiotic healing power, it naturally heals the illnesses and injuries of its practitioners.

In Kiryo healing, the Kiryo healer emits Kiryo life energy from his or her ku-no-ji palm, stimulates and awakens the recipient's nervous system,

---

[3] Ku no ji in Japanese literally means "the ku character" which looks like this > in Japanese.

and triggers it to produce its own Kiryo life energy. Thus, the Kiryo practitioner draws out and heightens the recipient's innate symbiotic healing power. As a result, the Kiryo patient's illnesses and injuries are healed, and health is restored. In other words, the patient's own symbiotic healing power becomes the primary healing force for their illnesses and injuries. When receiving Kiryo healing, it is essential that one feel and be as they are.

vague

In sum, Kiryo departs from the ideology that holds Ki to be a body-external natural energy, that exists everywhere and is possessed by all people, towards an ideology that considers a body-internal Ki known as the symbiotic healing power (Kiryo life energy). That is, it holds that the symbiotic healing power is innate to and shared by all people. This force is nothing but the healing sensory function that we humans have forgotten how to use.

Thanks to the establishment of Kiryo theory, Kiryo now has as its foundation the idea of the body-internal Ki: the symbiotic healing power.

A Word from the Author

If we take the restorative treatment made possible by stem cells to be the cutting edge of modern treatment, we can therefore say that Kiryo is a form of natural treatment made possible by the activity of the Kiryo nervous system centered around the primitive brainstem.

Chapter 1: The Healing Sensory Function Forgotten by Humans

1. Classifying Ki into Two General Categories

How should we capture the vague and boundless world of Ki? This is a difficult question. To aid in this venture, I would like to divide Ki into two broad concepts. The first is the *general concept* of Ki, and the second is the concept of a *healing* Ki.

(1) There are no Phrases for the Concept of Ki that Heals Illness and Injury

As we speak Japanese in our daily lives, we rather casually use the word "Ki" in compounds and phrases in both conversation and in writing. Maybe you have noticed this?

For example, phrases like "stay in good spirits," or "take care," which contain the word "Ki,"[4] are used in everyday conversations. Over the years, I have made a note of phrases containing the word Ki as I happened to notice them. Consequently, I realized just how many phrases there are in Japanese that use the word Ki.

From the conversational to the academic, and in every field in between, "Ki" is used. From the macroscopic to the microscopic, Ki is used to discuss countless phenomena. We use phrases with the word Ki often unconsciously. However, there are no phrases that refer to a Ki that can heal

---

[4]The phrases being referenced here by Kanzawa contain the word "Ki" when written in Japanese.

illness and injury.

(2) In Search of the True Nature of the Concept of a Healing Ki

Because there did not exist any concept of Ki healing in Japan, getting people to understand the idea of healing itself as it pertains to the healing of illness and injury was quite difficult. However, it is a cold, hard, irrefutable fact that illness and injury can be healed with Ki. By the way, in America, as in other parts of the world, Ki is recognized as a supplementary, alternative treatment.

Nowadays, with Japan having entered the age of integrative healing, the ears of the average Japanese person have become more accustomed to hearing the word "Ki" in the context of supplementary, alternative treatment, and I feel resistance towards the concept itself has lessened.

Thus, to seek the true nature (source) of the concept of a healing method that is effective in preventing or healing illness and injury, I would like to separate our discussions into two headings: that of the concept of a healing Ki centered around cognitive activity, and that of the concept of a healing Ki centered around healing sensory activity. - *Too much*

Splitting of concepts

(1) The Concept of a Ki Centered Around Thought Activity

We, as cognitive (linguistic) humans, live around the cognitive and nervous activity of our cerebra. Consequently, we can then search for the true nature (source) of the concept of a healing Ki in cognitive activity chiefly governed by thought as well as in nervous activity chiefly governed by feelings.

For instance, people often bring up the example of absorbing universal or solar energy through praying for good health as leading to the healing of illness and injury. Creativity and ingenuity centered around thoughts and the nerves can recover and restore illness and injury and prevent their future occurrence.

But what happens when we think of this healing Ki as a form of energy? At the end of the day, the energy manipulated and enhanced by

6

creativity and ingenuity brought about by thoughts and feelings constitutes the utilization of energy, or Ki, sought from outside the body.

(2) The Concept of a Ki Centered Around Healing Sensory Activity

We humans, whose entire existence is centered around the cognitive activities of our cerebrum, possess five sensory functions: sight, sound, smell, taste, and touch. We use our five sensory organs—eyes, ears, nose, tongue, and skin—as we lead our lives. However, we humans possess yet another sensory function: the healing sensory function centered around the brainstem that lies dormant within us. In other words, though we possess a life energy that is an energy meant to maintain our lives, at the same time, we also possess within our bodies a variation of that energy: a healing life energy that combats illness.

These energies—"life-energy" and "healing life-energy"—are forms of Ki. The wellspring, or source, of this Ki is our living brain, our brainstem.

The brainstem is characterized by homeostasis, which is a drive to always keep oneself alive. During our daily lives, we ceaselessly emit the Ki (life and healing life energies) which is sourced from the brainstem.

The Ki (life and healing life energies) emanated by us cannot be viewed or seen by our eyes. We also, initially, have no sense or awareness of the emission of this Ki. However, we latently possess the ability to perceive and differentiate with our ku-no-ji palms (refer to Illustration 2 on page 101) the Ki emanating from other people, animals, or plants. Further, with the Ki emitted from the *Ku No Ji* palm, one can heal these various organisms.

In other words, we live while emitting Ki (life and healing life energies) from our entire body. Our especially sensitive ku-no-ji palm possesses the ability to also emit and perceive/differentiate Ki as well. This is the healing sensory ability, centered around the brainstem, which heals injury and illness.

Here, let us consider the healing sensory function that perceives and differentiates Ki.

It would seem that there are only a small number of people who know of the existence of the healing sensory function that both perceives

7

1. Narrowing the source of life energy to a single physiological location is dangerous business

and differentiates Ki through the ku-no-ji palm. Additionally, there appears to be no concept of a healing sensory function in modern medical science or among the general population as a whole. *NO SHIT ?!*

To note, I also believe that it is nearly impossible to fully capture the healing sensory function with the creativity and ingenuity of linguistic or logical thought.

Heightening our healing sensory function throughout our entire body is difficult, though we can still utilize it to an effective degree in the palms of our hands and the soles of our feet by making ourselves able to sense Ki. The most important thing when doing this is to purge oneself of linguistic and logical thought, simply and consistently, feeling as one is.

In other words, Kiryo exercise and Kiryo healing are simply practices where one uses the ku-no-ji palm or sole of the foot to aid a "feel as you are" mentality towards Ki.

This is because this "feeling as you are" mentality is the greatest way that healing sensory function can be heightened and improved. "Feeling as you are" is like entering into a world of healing sensory function where linguistic and logical thoughts about Ki are not needed and are merely impediments.

To help you understand the applications as well as to validify this topic, I have real-life examples that showcase the existence of the healing sensory function. One can look to several television programs aired over a period of ten years on various networks that feature demonstrations I've been asked to perform. [see Author's biography at the end of this book for more information]

These programs involved countless Ki exchanges performed between me and animals that ranged in size from small to large. When Ki exchange between me and the animals began, a healing space, known as *Kiryo space*, was formed. Inside this space, the animals began to feel comforted, and therefore, would relax and lay down, eventually slipping into what's known as *Kiryo sleep*.

I transmitted Ki (life and healing life energy) through my right ku-no-ji palm, into these animals as they were inside the Kiryo space. The animals receive this Ki stimulation from me, and then lay down feeling comforted, and eventually slip into Kiryo sleep.

All I did to these animals was put my ku-no-ji palm (right hand) into a "feel as it is" state and move it right-to-left in a hand-waving motion. I would periodically still my hand as well. I simply repeated cycles of hand-waving and stillness. The hand-waving caused the animals to be able to more strongly perceive and differentiate the stimulation of my Ki that I was emitting.

The healing sensory capabilities of these animals that enabled them to sense my invisible Ki, far surpasses that of us cognitive (thought-based) humans to a seemingly unimaginable extent.

Kiryo exercise, Kiryo healing, and even the Kiryo healing of animals are all healing sensory activities that awaken our own healing sensory functions. This healing sensation is the beginning of the world of healing sensory function.

Why exactly have we humans forgotten how to use this healing sensory function centered around our brainstems? I believe the secret to this question lies in the history of the brainstem and the history of the cerebrum.

2. The History of the Brainstem and the History of the Cerebrum

(1) The Primeval Age Where the Brainstem was the Centerpoint

Before humanity began to walk on two legs, it is thought that we lived by relying on the sensory activity of the brainstem. Humanity is believed to have existed in a harsh natural environment coping with fierce struggles for existence and constant battles with illness.

Furthermore, just like other animals, humans resided at some relative position on the food chain. In order to protect themselves, it is thought that humans, like other animals, perceived and differentiated life energy with their whole body, a more primal skill which we've all but lost today, though it can still be found in animals.

Additionally, humanity used its brainstem as the centerpoint to emit Ki (life and healing life energies) as part of daily life. Somewhere along the way, humanity, possibly beginning with its switch to bipedalism, took the first

9

step in the long process of human evolution and began to lose this sensory ability.

(2) Development and Evolution of the Cerebrum

Ever since humanity began to walk on two legs, our hands were freed; allowing us to focus on holding and grasping things. In order to better obtain prey, this boon then naturally translated to the construction of weapons and tools.

It is thought that this capacity to create and use tools heightened our learning ability and encouraged the development of our cognitively-focused cerebrum. Through the evolution of this thinking brain, humanity developed advanced intellectual and cognitive functions which led it to build the advanced civilized societies of the modern age.

On a related note, the "primitive cerebrum" refers to the cerebrum as it was just when its development and evolution was beginning.

(3) The Cerebrum's Acquisition of Two Functions

We consider the cerebrum to have acquired, broadly speaking, two functions through the course of its evolution from its primitive to its current, modern form. These are its *intellectual function* and its *suppressive function*.

The Acquisition of the Brain's Intelligence Ability

The scholastically advanced present human race acquired linguistic abilities through the evolution of the cerebrum. This linguistic ability is an example of linguistically-mediated cognitive activity.

Language—the use of speech or writing as a means of expressing, transmitting, and understanding thoughts, emotions, and intentions—heightened our cerebral function. This elevated cerebral function allowed for the civilized societies of today. Further, I feel that the cognitively motivated expansion of the cerebrum was additionally spurred by the advances in

10

society it itself was bringing about. As the years continue, the cognitive functions of our cerebra will only continue to grow ever-more specific and exact.

(2) The Acquisition of the Cerebrum's Suppressive Function

It is said that the human brain is made up of an old brain and a new brain. The old brain is centered around the brainstem. The new brain is the cerebrum; the part of the brain that, over the course of its evolution, helped to build the civilized society we live in today.

The old brain and the new brain evolved together to create a feedback system that controlled excitement and suppression. In other words, the new brain and the old brain evolved by repeatedly exciting and suppressing each other, all to maintain harmony or a functionable homeostasis. The harmony I speak of here is largely based around suppression.

It is thought that during the development and evolution of the cerebrum, alongside cerebral function, we also gained a suppressive function. The cognitive activity that defines us modern humans is made possible by the suppressive function of the cerebrum. In particular, the reason our five senses are able to function in accordance with the demands of our living environments is because of the suppressive capability of the cerebrum. If any of our five senses became far more sensitive than the others, we would have a difficult time going about our lives. This potential for excessive sensitivity is what is suppressed and controlled by the suppressive function of the cerebrum. The reason we can sharpen our five senses is due to the cerebrum's suppressive capability.

The brain, while evolving, inhibited the old brainstem (the primitive brainstem) and forced it to evolve into the modern brainstem: sealing away the healing sensory function. As a result, we lost the ability to feel the life and healing life energies of people, animals, and plants. This sealed healing sensory function is the world of *healing sensation* that has been forgotten by humans. In effect, we hold a world with an entirely different dimension and capacity latently within our bodies.

Let us now consider the latent healing sensory function that we

11

humans possess within us from the perspective of the relationship between the suppressive function of the cerebrum and the brainstem.

(4) The Two Functions of the Cerebrum Concealed the Healing Sensory Function

The brainstem evolved alongside the evolution of the primitive cerebrum. However, in order for humanity to become the race of thinking beings we are today, a certain relationship was necessitated between the cerebrum and the brainstem. The cerebrum forced the brainstem to evolve into the modern brainstem so that we can live as human beings whose activities are centered around cognitive, or cerebrum, based processes. As a result, the primitive brainstem was veiled, and it now resides, for the most part, latently as genetic information.

Specifically, the two cerebral functions that suppressed the brainstem are the intellectual function (cognitive activities) and the suppressive function.

These two abilities of the cerebrum are what sealed the healing sensory function centered around the primitive brainstem so that we could no longer feel the invisible life energy around us. Consequently, we humans, in general, have no idea about this healing sensory function. This is what is referred to by the phrase "the healing sensory function forgotten by humans"—the world of healing sensation.

Does this mean that we've lost the healing sensory function in our bodies? Of course not.

Due to the suppressive function of the cerebrum, it is difficult for someone to experience or feel life and healing life energies with their entire body (this limitation does not apply to persons suffering from chronic illnesses). However, by diligently practicing Kiryo exercise and Kiryo healing, one can regain the ability to feel life and healing life energies in the palm of the hand and the sole of the foot then eventually elsewhere.

In particular, and initially, it is possible to feel invisible Ki (life and healing life energies) with the palms of the very hands that built our civilized societies. Specifically, we can make our fingers—concentrated as they are with capillary blood vessels—capable of feeling this Ki.

In Kiryo, we use our five fingers and palm to form the *ku-no-ji palm*. Why? Because by using our five fingers and palm to form the ku-no-ji palm, the entire hand becomes capable of feeling Ki. We can also develop the ability to faintly feel Ki in the soles of our feet.

In the next chapter, I will focus on nervous activity, and I'll theoretically expand on the foundations of the brainstem and the suppressive function of the cerebrum.

Chapter 2: Kiryo Focuses on the Activity of the Nerves

1. Searching for the Origin of Sensory Healing:

(1) "Feeling as You Are" Is How One Enters the World of Healing Sensation

As explained in Chapter 1, the evolution and development of the cerebrum enabled humans to build civilization and culture. Having spurred on the development and advancement of science and medicine, we now reap the benefits. In particular, the public consensus is that it is because of this progress that we have conquered many infectious diseases (epidemics). In fact, for humans today, reverence of and dependence on Western medicine is absolutely natural and generally expected.

We live in an age where people see a doctor even when they catch a cold. It's strange that, not too long ago, you might hear an expression like, "there is no better medicine than sleep," and it was understood that our bodies were capable of handling most minor illnesses. However, the reality is that today, despite possessing the powers of both Western and Eastern medicine, the end of illness is still nowhere in sight. Quite the contrary, in fact: illness is on the rise.

With its rapidly declining birth-rate and aging society, it is inevitable that Japan will one day become a society highlighted by its great number of elderly and ill people. The ballooning of healthcare and nursing costs walks hand in hand with this issue, exacerbating the overall health problem. Our next great battle will not be fought with weapons against some physical foe, but against illness itself.

14

The important questions are: What is the best course of action for defeating these eventualities? How can we decisively route illness itself?

The Japanese government, recognizing the realities of a declining birthrate and an aging population, and worrying for the future of Japan, promulgated the *Health Promotion Act* on August 2, 2002. Article 2 of this law establishes that, as part of their duty as citizens, the people of Japan should make an effort to take care of their own health.

Codifying into law the ideal that one should take care of one's own health showcases a profound concern for the future of Japan. On the foundations of the Health Promotion Act, the country—its prefectures, cities, towns, and villages, and the people that inhabit them—has undertaken many mutually cooperative efforts to implement various plans, and it's currently working with clear determination towards advancing the health of Japan's citizens.

However, I cannot help but notice that at present, there doesn't currently exist any definite plans to heighten the symbiotic healing power and life force that all human beings innately possess.

Why is that? The answer may be comfort.

As I explained in Chapter 1, the development and evolution of the cerebrum enabled us to grasp the reality of many aspects of this world in a way we previously couldn't, thereby further spurring the growth of the thinking brain—the cerebrum—while causing the weakening of the living brain—the brainstem. Humans, as such, have become able to distance themselves from the harshness of nature and providence and now live comfortable lives amidst civilization.

Yet this exchange has also placed us into what is known as a stress society: a society that is inundated by stress, a society that inherently spawns excessive quantities of stress in its citizens. Since the originally present function of the brainstem has grown quite weak in its influence, our ability to fight against illness has weakened.

Only revitalization of the brainstem can preserve and heighten the life force, and also heighten the symbiotic life force. In essence, Ki energy is life force and symbiotic life force. Drawing out and heightening Ki energy is a definite method of achieving health promotion.

We live in a cognitive world. However, there is a need for humans—

within the context of health promotion—to once again awaken the world of sensation that we've forgotten. The world of the senses *is* the healing sensory world.

So, how can we awaken and enter the world of healing sensation?

The method for this, as already outlined, involves feeling Ki as you are, and to be as you are inside of Ki itself. There is no other way to enter the world of healing sensation, and the world of healing sensation is the world of Kiryo itself.

The world of Kiryo is one of feeling and being as you are. There is no need to attempt to manipulate or control Ki. Further, creativity and ingenuity are not necessary. Kiryo is the process of becoming one with the natural energy that is Ki. This unification is what vitalizes the brainstem and what eventually leads to the world of strong healing sensation itself.

The spirit of Kiryo is one of naturalness: simply feeling and being as you are. Willpower, concentration, meditation, visualization, ideation, breathing techniques, body movement exercises, and the like are not necessary in the world of Kiryo. Quite the opposite, in fact: they impede one's entry into the world of Kiryo. Kiryo is simply, purely, and constantly feeling and being as you are.

A single question should nicely tie together everything I have discussed thus far: should one think or feel to experience Ki and Ki energy? The answer this question will lead one into either the world of cognition, or the world of healing sensation. It is where the path forks.

Kiryo chooses the latter: to feel, to sense. The sensory world is the world of healing sensation, the world that is the source of life. In a word, "feeling as you are" is everything in Kiryo. It is a primary maxim of Kiryo theory.

One's life outside of Kiryo can, of course, be spent in the world of thought. We can easily switch between the two. When we are not performing Kiryo exercise or Kiryo healing, many generally return to their usual daily lives in the world of thought.

(2) Nervous Activity is the Foundation of Kiryo:

16

When I was first awakened to Kiryo, I felt something abnormal in the palms of my hands. Even when I was not touching anything, I still felt a cool, blowing sensation: as if a wind was passing directly through my hand, from the palm to the back.

What in the world was this cool, blowing sensation in the palm of my hand??

This simple but baffling question led me to the discovery of the incredible healing sensory world of Ki.

I kept pondering this cool, blowing sensation I felt in the palm of my hand. I spent many days wondering at its strangeness. On one such day, I pointed my hand towards a part of my father's shoulder, a part where there was pain, and I waved it back and forth, the whole movement coming naturally. Upon doing so, his pain somehow went away.

Somewhat in disbelief, I came to him the next morning and asked him how his shoulder felt. "It does not hurt!", he exclaimed, while rolling his shoulder around. This was the beginning of Kiryo healing, and specifically, partner Kiryo.

After that, many miraculous healings occurred. Yet, I eventually began worrying over how one could best comprehend the actions and effects of this healing. After some time, this train of thought led me to the realization that because the cool, blowing feeling in my palm was a sort of sensation, it might have some relationship with the sensory nerves. This was the beginning of what spurred me to direct my focus towards nervous activity.

Interestingly, the word "nerve" in Japanese, "shinkei," was coined by Genpaku Sugita; a scholar of Dutch medicine who lived in the middle Edo period[5]. Genpaku translated a Dutch medical text and called the completed work "New Text on Anatomy," and came up with the term during his translation. Apparently, he coined it from the characters used to write the words "divine energy"—the force that makes up all things—and "vessel"—the term used for the blood vessels of the human body).

---

[5]The Edo period in Japanese history was between 1603 and 1868.

17

The text treats "divine energy" as a concept in which Ki is the foundation for all things in the universe, and "vessels" are composed of the blood and the vessels that carry it—both things indispensable to the human body. I focused on the activity of the nerves while being completely ignorant of this definition and was surprised to eventually discover that it and my own conceptions aligned so closely.

The first character of the Japanese word for nerve, "shinkei", is "shin," which refers to the universe (nature), while the second character, "kei," refers to the human body. Thus, nerve/shinkei signifies a relationship between the universe (nature) and the human body. A spectacularly important word indeed.

I was again surprised that the concept of Ki was so central to the concept of the nerve itself. It has only been 240 years since the word nerve ("shinkei") was first introduced into modern Japanese language. Using a focus on nervous activity to grasp the world of Ki was all but impossible prior to this introduction.

(3) There Is Undiscovered Power within the Kiryo Nervous System

The Human Nervous System in Conventional Medicine

The nerves are made up of bundles of nerve fibers which are thread-like organs that both transmit excitatory[6] impulses from the central nervous system to all of its parts and transmit stimuli from the parts of the body to the core.

The central nervous system is made up of the brain and spinal cord. The peripheral nerves are the nerves that connect the brain, the spinal cord, and the entire body to each other.

The peripheral nerves are composed of the cranial nerves and the spinal nerves. The peripheral nerves can be divided, according to their

---

[6]A word that is commonly used in neuroscience to refer to impulses that excite, or activate, a neuron or tissue.

18

function, into the somatic and autonomic nerves. The somatic nerves are involved in the activity of the body and can be further divided into the sensory and motor nerves.

The somatic sensory nerves are nerves that communicate to the central nervous system information received when seeing (optic nerves), hearing (auditory nerves), smelling (olfactory nerves), tasting (gustatory nerves), and touching (tactile nerves). On the other hand, the motor nerves transmit movement commands from the brain to all parts of the body.

These are the main nerves that compose the nervous system according to modern medical science.

The Birth of Kiryo Terminology in the Verbalizing of Sensory Phenomena

As I have explained earlier, I was awakened to the concept of Ki, and realized that the cool, blowing feeling I felt in my hands might be due to a type of sensory nerve. This process was what spurred me to focus on nervous activity.

Nowadays, we live in an age where even nerves can be constructed anew from pluripotent stem cells. That is an impressive achievement, however, unaware as they are of the world of Ki, neurological researchers remain blind to the grander relationship nerves have with Ki. By comprehensively improving nervous function, Ki can influence the mind and body resulting in remarkable feats of healing on the human body's physiological framework.

I would like to make something clear. I am not a Ki physician or scientist. I am but a single Kiryo practitioner engaging in the research and investigation of Ki.

Because the world of Ki is a world of "feeling as you are" and "being as you are"—a world of healing sensation—, for a long time there were no words in Japanese or logic to describe it. However, in Kiryo healing (two-person Kiryo), in the classroom, or during Kiryo exercise in other places, various phenomena would still frequently occur. I labored long and hard, with no small measure of worry, as to how to translate these phenomena into words. Eventually, I developed Kiryo terminology. Examples include, "Ki response sensation," "primitive brainstem," "Kiryo nerves," "perceptive

19

differentiation nerve," "sensory stiffening nerve," "Kiryo space," "primitive cerebrum," "other-person healing ability," and "symbiotic healing power."

(4) From the Cognitive World, Once Again into the Sensory

Some may think that by discussing "a return into the world of sensation," I am advocating that we go back once again to our lifestyles in the primeval age which I discussed in Chapter 1. This is obviously not my intent. Kiryo seeks to heal illness and injury, and to promote health such that one may be guarded against future illness as well. Kiryo revolves around a unification with the natural energy known as Ki. Kiryo is "feeling as you are" and "being as you are" in Ki. Kiryo is purely a world of sensation.

Now, then, it is time to step foot into the world of the sensation that humans forgot: the world of healing sensation.

Please take a look at Figure 1 on page 22. This figure contains pictorial representations of the concepts I have discussed up till now. Moving on, let us now experience the fundamentals of feeling the natural energy known as Ki.

How to Experience Ki

Hand feedback Sensation)

1) Sit with your legs folded underneath you or with your legs crossed. You can also sit in a chair or stand: wherever or however you choose.

2) Keep your elbows close to your sides.

3) Elevate your palms to the level of your elbows, and rotate them so they face upwards.

4) Keep your four fingers and thumb together (keep your five fingers together).

5) Shape your palm and fingers such that they form the ku-no-ji when viewed from the side.

6) Apply a slight amount of effort to ensure that your fingers stay together in this ku no ji shape.

7) Maintain your awareness in this state.

8) Eventually, you will become aware of a slight, sensation-like change in your palms.

9) Allow yourself to feel that sensation as you are.

10) That feeling in your hands—the hand feedback sensation— is the natural energy that is Ki.

11) By allowing this state to continue, you will unify yourself with the natural energy.

Numbers 1-11 above are the ordered steps by which one may experience Ki. Regardless of whether or not you can actually feel Ki while in it, when in the state of Step 11 above, you have taken your first step into the world of the healing sensation humans have forgotten. In certain cases, it may be that the nerves that enable you to perceive and differentiate Ki are still at rest and have not been vitalized.

To help elucidate this, we may look to the fact that almost all children possess the ability to perceive Ki. As they age, that ability is gradually put to sleep by the activity of their cerebra. For example, if I were to hold a "Ki Health Class" for the lower grades of primary school, and teach those children Ki exercise, almost all of them would be able to feel and even master Ki energy. The reason is that, like animals, children at the beginning of their growth lead their lives centered around the brainstem then are drawn away into the cerebrum by society.

Figure 1: The Healing Sensory Function Forgotten by Humanity

The Sensory World (Physiological Function)	The Cognitive World (Cognitive Function)
Body-Internal Ki	**Body-External Ki**
The Symbiotic Healing Power (Kiryo Life Energy)	**Universal Energy, etc.**
(Healing Sensory Function)	**Willpower**
The Primitive Brainstem	**Concentration**
The Kiryo Nerves	**Meditation**
	Visualization
Sensory Stiffening Nerve / Perceptive Differentiation Nerve	**Ideation**
	Breathing Techniques
(The Kiryo Nervous System)	**Gymnastics**
The Ki Response Sensation (Feel as You Are)	**Creativity and Ingenuity**

⬑ Perception
↑
Ki

22

Once those children grow up, they will probably benefit from greatly reduced medical fees. As another way to prove the ability of people to feel Ki, one may point to the fact that in patients who suffer from chronic illnesses their entire body is thirsting for Ki.

Eighty percent of people who are ill can feel Ki on the soles of their feet, the palms of their hands, or their whole body. Conversely, healthy people do not feel Ki. The reason for this is that in their balanced, healthy state, they have no need to feel Ki. However, even healthy people can become able to understand the existence of Ki through Kiryo exercise.

If one merely attempts to notice the existence of Ki, one can enter the sensory world at any time. It's only now that I fully understand the true nature of the cool, blowing feeling I feel in my palms. Despite being completely unaware of it, the sensations are my Kiryo nerves working automatically to allow me to realize the natural energy of Ki.

Ever since I felt that sensation, I have been in the world of the sensory. It took me nearly twenty years to understand this fact.

2. Kiryo is the Origin of Healing

(1) Focusing on Nervous Activity is a Landmark Development

Kiryo focuses on the activity of the nerves, this is its foundation. I personally believe this to be an epochal, correct development. After my brainstem shock—which I'll explain—the cool, blowing feeling in my hands then caused me to focus on nervous activity, and now, after twenty-four years of ups and downs, I have returned, yet again, to the brainstem.

In writing this book, I was put into the rather uncomfortable position of having to detail the nature of my brainstem shock because Kiryo theory cannot stand without the elucidation and explanation of this concept. After much investigation, I arrived at the conclusion that the power of Ki resides in the brainstem, and that the wellspring of this power is the primitive brainstem which lies within the modern brainstem. And so, with that said, I'll discuss what I call my brainstem shock.

My brainstem shock happened in 1988 at the sort of midnight hour

I generally spend fast asleep. Suddenly, from within my sleep, I felt a boom!-like shock inside my head, and the moment my eyes snapped open, I felt a shockwave pass through my body. I thought of getting up at that time, but I ended up falling asleep again.

Throughout that day, that shock occurred a total of six times. This brainstem shock was the awakening of the Kiryo nervous system centered around the brainstem. The brainstem shock is the origin of Kiryo itself.

(2) Discovery of a Nervous System Based Around the Primitive Brainstem

Through my shock experience, I learned about the activity of the primitive brainstem and the activity of nerves unexplained in modern medical science. There are three of these unexplained peripheral nerves.

The first is the *Kiryo nerve*: the nerve for the power of Ki (the power of healing). The second is the *perceptive differentiation nerve*: the nerve that perceives and differentiates various types of Ki (life and healing life energies). The third is the *sensory stiffening nerve* which softens and adjusts the muscles. Just as we say that we must "fight fire with fire," in the case of the muscles, we must "fight stiffness with stiffness." The sensory stiffening nerve, as if wringing them out, stiffens tight muscles and then relaxes them.

The activity of the primitive brainstem causes these three peripheral nerves—not to be found in modern medical science—to activate. Normally, we do not use these nerves, and as such, they remain dormant. The primitive brainstem and these three peripheral nerves together contain an incredibly powerful, undiscovered life defense system.

This undiscovered life defense system protects life and heals illness and injury. Additionally, this undiscovered life defense system performs the bodily, constitutional improvements that enable heightening of the symbiotic healing power, life force, and vital force. It also prevents the occurrence of illness while promoting general health.

In conclusion, humans have merely forgotten the existence of the primitive brainstem and these three peripheral nerves, though we can easily awaken them and begin to utilize them by performing Ki (life and healing-

24

life energies) exchange: a practice I will explain in detail in the coming chapters.

(3) The Wellspring of Ki Energy Was Always the Primitive Brainstem

Thus far, I have elaborated on the activity of the nerves in relation to Kiryo, and I've explained the influence Kiryo has on the body. I have also commented on the history of the cerebrum and the history of the brainstem, and so surmised that the primitive natures of the cerebrum and brainstem have been inherited, unbroken and continuously, in the form of genetic memories carved into these organs.

I have phenomenologically explained and deduced, through Kiryo healing and Kiryo exercise, the effects and examples mentioned above. As a result, I learned that the power of Ki resides inside the brainstems we live with today, after realizing that the capabilities of the primitive brainstem still exist inside our current brainstems and have gone on to prove its existence.

The wellspring of Ki energy has always been in the primitive brainstem. The existence of the primitive brainstem is not directly recognized by modern medical science. However, when phenomenologically examining Kiryo, we conclude that the capacities of the primitive brainstem still lie dormant within our current, modern brainstems. Furthermore, this analysis also makes clear the existence of a healing nervous system based on the brainstem. This primitive brainstem and healing nervous system (Kiryo nervous system) act as a formidable life defense system.

As our intelligence develops, our cerebra evolve to become ever-more complex. As this expansion continues, the balance between the activity of the cerebrum and the activity of the brainstem worsens. The relationship is already bad, yet the expansion only continues this negative trend. Simply put, the cognitive expansion of the cerebrum leads to the weakening of the activity of the brainstem.

A substantial cause for this is what we commonly refer to as stress. Stress is mental strain brought about by the cognitive activity of the cerebrum. Continued mental strain leads to what we refer to as *built-up stress*.

I believe that cognitive expansion of the cerebrum will continue to bolster and grow the stress society we live in today. This stress society weakens our brainstem's activity: the cognitive expansion of the cerebrum brings with it the vital weakening of the brainstem.

The development and evolution of the cerebrum occurred to help achieve the goal of protection, to protect us from the harsh, dog-eat-dog conditions of the ancient world, from things like predators and infectious diseases. Now, cognitive expansion is showing itself as damage upon vital functions, a damage can be seen in our fights with illness. Many infamous infectious diseases have been brought to heel, but we have weakened in our battles with other illnesses, and the numbers of the ill are increasing.

What should we do about the unbalancing between our cerebrum and brainstem?

Harmony and balance between the cerebrum and brainstem will be achieved when the brainstem is made wholesome. The *wholesome brainstem* enables us to defeat illness and protect against its future occurrence.

The way to make the brainstem wholesome is to awaken the primitive brainstem and put it to use. The primitive brainstem lives on inside our current brainstems, slumbering soundly deep within. This primitive brainstem has a vigorous, strong life force: it is the wellspring of Ki energy itself.

There is a way to awaken the Ki energy of the brainstem, and it's quite simple. In fact, it is so simple that many of us haven't realized it as a possibility. This method takes place in Kiryo exercise and Kiryo healing. You can do Kiryo exercise alone, but it is during person-to-person Ki (healing life energy) exchange that the primitive brainstem's Ki energy can best be awakened. What happens is that the two participants exchange their Ki energy (healing life energy) with each other.

At its core, Kiryo exercise is the practice of exchanging Ki (healing life energy) between one participant's ku-no-ji palm and the other participant's ku-no-ji palm. No method or way of thought that aims to strictly train the brainstem is needed. All that one needs to do is feel the Ki (healing life energy) being exchanged through their ku-no-ji palm.

Ki (healing life energy) exchange can be done among family members, friends, or even acquaintances. As long the participants remember to feel as they are, they can, even while talking, practice and improve their Ki power.

Ki exercise can also be carried out by members of the local community in public facilities, like community centers and gymnasiums, where they can gather in large numbers and practice. In environments like this, large healing Kiryo spaces can be created. Of course, weather permitting, this can also be done in open spaces like public parks.

In summary, by exchanging Ki (healing life energy) with individuals who are *feeling as they are*, people can awaken their primitive brainstems. Awakening the primitive brainstem in this way continually strengthens its vital functions.

This allows for victory over illness, prevention of future illness, and overall health promotion. The mind and body are made wholesome through restoration of harmony between the cerebrum and the brainstem. This is the origin of Kiryo.

Chapter 3: Awaken Your Primitive Brainstem

Physiology from the Perspective of Kiryo

Kiryo theory is formulated from a combination of the knowledge of modern medical science and the experience and practice of Ki healing, including Kiryo exercise. Without the knowledge of modern medicine, Kiryo and Kiryo theory cannot stand.

Because everyone possesses Ki, since ancient times, people who harnessed Ki energy (healing life energy) were found all over the country. However, in eras that lacked the vocabulary to properly theorize it, the phenomenon of Ki was regarded either with mystery or as some form of supernatural ability.

Though, today, thanks to modern medicine, we are able to properly theorize and define Kiryo. Please refer to Figure 2 on page 29, "The Makeup of the Human Body in Kiryo", where I have summarized the organization of the human body from the perspective of Kiryo. As has been mentioned before, I thought that the "cool, blowing feeling" in the palm of the hand was due to a type of sensory nerve. That was the beginning of the shift of my focus to nervous activity.

In Figure 2, I have broadly divided the human body into four parts. The row headings for this figure are such, from top to bottom: we have the bones, the muscles, the fluids, and the nerves. The bones, as part of the skeletal framework, support the physique, allow for the attachment of the muscles, protect the organs and conduct movement.

Figure 2: The Makeup of the Human Body in Kiryo

Parts	Makeup of the Human Body (Structures)			
Bones	Skeleton	Support of the Physique	Protection of Organs Facilitation of Movement	
Muscles	Skeletal Muscles	Attached to the Skeleton	Voluntary Muscles	
	Visceral Muscles	Various Internal Organs	Involuntary Muscles	
	Other	-	-	
Fluids	Bodily Fluids (Tissue Fluid)	Blood	Blood Cells	Red Blood Cells
				White Blood Cells
			Platelets	
		Hormones	Each Type of Hormone	
		Other Fluids	Cerebrospinal Fluid, etc.	
Nerves	Central Nerves	Brain	Cerebrum	
			Cerebellum	
			Modern Brainstem (Primitive Brainstem)	
		Spinal Cord	Nervous Junction	
	Main Peripheral Nerves	Cranial Nerves	Vagus Nerve, etc.	
		Spinal Nerves	Autonomic Nerves	Sympathetic Nerves
				Parasympathetic Nerves
			Sensory Nerves	Five Sensory Nerves, Etc.
			Motor Nerves	Motor Functions
		Kiryo Nerves	Perceptive Differentiation Nerve	Perceptive/Differentiative Power
			Sensory Stiffening Nerve	Sensory Stiffening Power

29

The muscles are broadly divided into the skeletal muscles and the visceral muscles. The skeletal muscles are voluntary muscles, and the visceral muscles are involuntary muscles. The fluids are the bodily fluids. By bodily fluids, I mean the fluid inside the vessels of the body, and the fluid that fills the gaps between tissues. Specifically, these fluids include the blood, the lymph fluids, hormones, and the cerebrospinal fluid that covers the brain and spinal cord, among others.

The nerves are divided into the central nerves and the peripheral nerves. The central nerves are the brain and the spinal cord.

The brain consists of the cerebrum, the cerebellum, and the modern brainstem (and the primitive brainstem). The spinal cord resides inside the spinal column. The spinal cord is an important central nerve which connects the brain with the peripheral nerves.

In Kiryo, because it ties together the nervous network of the body with the brain at its center, the spinal cord is referred to as the *nervous junction*. The spinal nerves can be divided into the autonomous nerves and the somatic nerves. The somatic nerves are concerned with the body and movement and can be divided into the sensory nerves and the motor nerves. All of this is common knowledge in modern medicine.

In the world of Kiryo, however, we hold that there exists a separate set of Kiryo nerves apart from the peripheral nerves known to modern medicine. These can be found at the very bottom of the figure, where they are labeled as such. These three nerves are referred to as the Kiryo nerve, the Sensory Stiffening Nerve, and the Perceptive Differentiation Nerve. These three Kiryo nerves are capable of bringing about highly-pronounced Kiryo effects against injury and illness and are equally capable of preventing illness as well. I will explain the details of these nerves later.

2. Discovering the Activity and Role of the Kiryo Nerves

As a result of having practiced Kiryo healing and Kiryo exercise, I have phenomenologically understood the wonderful healing effects Ki energy (healing life energy) can have on the body.

Following this, I pondered for a long time how best to categorize and express the concepts of Ki energy. As a result, I now know that the essence of Ki energy is to be found in nervous function.

Consequently, I have turned my attention to the structure and makeup of the nerves. Upon examining their structure, one can see that the nerves are made up of bundles of nerve fibers. In modern general medicine, Ki energy (healing life energy) doesn't exist, but, from a phenomenological perspective, the existence of Ki comes as an undeniable fact.

Drawing from what I'd come to know, I concluded that Ki energy (healing life energy) must reside in some way within the bundles of nerve fibers inside the nerves. Though I grappled for a time with how best to name it, I eventually decided that because the nerves in question contained Ki energy inside them, they should be called the *Kiryo nerves*. These Kiryo nerves have become central to Kiryo theory. Next, I'll discuss the activity and role of the Kiryo nerves.

(1) Nervous Activity is the Foundation of Kiryo

Kiryo understands the world of Ki through nervous activity and heals injury and illness through nervous activity. Further, Ki energy, perceptive/differentiative power, and sensory stiffening power are all forms of nervous activity, and anyone can master them.

Broadly speaking, the activities of the Kiryo nerves are as follows: to heal illness and injury, and to make the mastery of both perceptive/differentiative power and sensory stiffening power possible. Further, these Kiryo nerves reside inside the bundles of nerve fibers within our bodies. These points are the foundation of Kiryo theory.

(2) Dividing Ki into the Cognitive and Sensory Worlds

I am proud to say that with the emergence of the concept of the Kiryo nerves, it became possible to divide the vague, vast, limitless world of Ki into manageable cognitive and sensory realms. As a result, the world of healing Ki within the sensory world has become far clearer.

31

In the cognitive world, various forms of creativity and ingenuity are employed to make active use of Ki energy. On the other hand, in the healing sensory world, Ki energy is only *felt as it is*. No cognitive processes are needed. One need only unify oneself with natural energy and feel and be as they are. That is it. This is the pure world of healing sensation. This is the world of Kiryo. Kiryo does not search outside of the body, but instead within the body, for the essence (source) of Ki. Kiryo is the pursuit of Ki through the primitive brainstem.

(3) The Kiryo Nerve is the Cornerstone of the Kiryo Nervous System

The existence of a nervous system unrecognized and undiscovered in modern medicine has been made plain through the phenomenology of healing. The Kiryo nervous system lies at the center of this unrecognized system, with the perceptive differentiation nerve and the sensory stiffening nerve alongside it.

These three peripheral nerves make up what we refer to as the Kiryo nervous system. The Kiryo nerve is the cornerstone of the Kiryo nervous system. This is because when the Kiryo nerve is awakened, the perceptive differentiation nerve and the sensory stiffening nerve are both simultaneously activated and begin to function.

(4) The Role of the Kiryo Nerve in Awakening the Primitive Brainstem

The brainstem shock experience that I previously discussed occurred to improve the constitution of my weak body. In truth, in my weakened body, my brainstem had, ever since I was a boy, been seeking and desiring Ki energy.

As I grew and matured, my Kiryo nerves, themselves manifestations of Ki, physiologically stimulated my brainstem. Through direct stimulation, my Kiryo nerves awakened the primitive brainstem that lay dormant inside my brainstem as a physiological memory. The shock that occurred throughout my body also simultaneously awakened the perceptive differentiation and sensory stiffening nerves that lay dormant inside the nerve fiber bundles within my body. That these phenomena occurred is an incontrovertible fact.

While they haven't experienced the brainstem shocks exactly as I did, there are many who underwent phenomenal experiences of recovery and restoration. What these people have in common is that they were all burdened with chronic sickness and suffered from pain for many years. Additionally, they all, despite the length of their illnesses and suffering, were able to recover and restore their health.

The idea of physiological memory is the concept that experiences undertaken by the body in the past have been physiologically recorded by the nerves. For instance, when undergoing Kiryo healing, some feel pain in bones they broke years before which were supposed to have completely healed. That pain will soon disappear. This is what is known as *phantom pain*. This illusionary pain is, in actuality, the nerves' memory of a past fracture.

I have been studying this field for over twenty years, and because of my work with Kiryo, I have focused on nervous function. The results of my studies lie not in the realm of modern medicine, but in the discovery of a Kiryo nervous system centered around the Kiryo nerve.

Moreover, I have been able to discover the primitive brainstem, which lies dormant within the modern brainstem as the wellspring of Ki energy (healing life energy). The Kiryo nerves, which correspond to the cranial nerves and the spinal nerves, are the primitive brainstem and the Kiryo peripheral nerves (perceptive differentiation nerve and sensory stiffening nerve).

3. The Activity and Role of the Perceptive Differentiation Nerve

(1) The Perceptive Differentiation Nerve Feels Invisible Healing Energy

Among the energies emitted from our physical bodies, there are life energy, healing energy, and affected part energy. Yet, why is it that we modern humans cannot feel these three energies with the palms of our hands, the soles of our feet, or anywhere in our bodies? I will explain three reasons for this.

The first is the fact that not much time has passed since Western medical science first discovered, through anatomical dissection, the existence of nerves. The second is that, in modern medicine, because healing life energy is not visible and does not appear in pictures or recordings, there is no concept of the phenomenon whatsoever. The third is that when it comes to healing life energy, no one had thought to understand the phenomenon by focusing on nervous activity.

Consequently, it is impossible for the sensory nervous system, as defined by modern medical science, to be capable of feeling or sensing life energy. For example, it is impossible to use any of the five senses—sight, hearing, smell, taste, or touch—to sense life energy.

In other words, it is impossible for our senses, according to modern medical science, to feel the life energy of the body. Consequently, most modern humans are simply unaware that the life energy being emitted by our bodies can be sensed with the palms of the hands, with the soles of the feet, or even with the entire body.

Under modern medicine's view of sense and perception, the invisible life energy of our bodies cannot be felt. There is a blind spot that exists in the results and achievements of modern medicine with respect to nervous activity. The findings of anatomical science are considered to be the first and last word in the study of the human nervous system and are what have entered common knowledge. In the nervous system of modern medical science, there are no healing nerves and no healing nervous system. However, when one begins to consider, or experience for themselves, the phenomenology of the healing that occurs in the body through Kiryo, it becomes undeniable that a healing nervous system exists: it is called the Kiryo nervous system.

One of the nerves in this system, the perceptive differentiation nerve, allows us to feel and distinguish the invisible energies of the body. All of us have this perceptive differentiation nerve. It merely lies dormant within us.

Therefore, we must awaken this slumbering perceptive differentiation nerve by *feeling as we are*. Upon being awakened, the perceptive differentiation nerve allows you to feel the invisible life energies emitted by the body. Furthermore, it lets you feel the existence of the Kiryo nervous system, the healing nervous system itself.

(2) Neurotransmissive Exchange: Neurotransmissive Exchange Outside the Body

"Neurotransmissive exchange outside the body" here refers to the neurotransmissive exchanges of Ki (healing life energy) that occur during Kiryo. Put another way, neurotransmissive exchange is, in Kiryo, nothing but neurostimulatory exchange. However, I can understand many people will find these claims hard to believe. Without truly experiencing it with one's own body, it is hard to even recognize the existence of neurotransmissive exchange outside the body. This is because, as was mentioned earlier, the fact that there exists a healing nervous system (Kiryo nervous system) within our bodies is almost unknown.

Moreover, in the nervous system of modern medicine, based on the findings of anatomical science, there is no healing nervous system. This means that it is almost expected that the average person does not know that there exists such a nervous system inside our bodies. Humans have truly forgotten about the world of healing sensation. Humans have forgotten about the healing nervous system (Kiryo nervous system).

Let us once again consider the nerves that correspond to our five senses. While living our daily lives, we see (optic nerve), hear (auditory nerve), smell (olfactory nerve), taste (gustatory nerve), and touch (tactile nerve). These five sensory nerves are for the stimuli of the outside world, the body-external world. We receive external stimuli through these sensory organs, whereby they are transmitted (conducted) inside our bodies by the nerves, and eventually reaching the brain. The brain processes these transmissions and then sends orders to our various body parts. We then act according to these orders.

Given this, it is not too difficult to imagine the following scenario occurring:

During a conversation with another we use our ears to listen to what is said and to help us form a response. In turn, the other person listens to that response with their ears. Thus, we can think of dialogue with another

35

as a form of neurotransmissive exchange outside the body conducted through the auditory nerves, can we not?

Similarly, can we not say that handshakes and the like are instances of neurotransmissive exchange outside of the body facilitated by tactile nerves? However, once the hand you are shaking moves about four inches away from your own, there is no longer any need for your tactile nerves to function. Yet, when the hands of you and your partner are about four inches apart, life energy is still being emitted from them. Now, let us assume that both of you would like to attempt to feel the healing life-energy you are emitting. If the activity of both of your perceptive differentiation nerves is weak, then, even if it is occurring, the exchange of healing life-energy will be almost imperceptible.

Yet, individuals whose perceptive differentiation nerve is strong and active will be able to perceive and differentiate the healing life energy exchange occurring. This perception and differentiation task is difficult for those with weak perceptive differentiation nerve activity. Individuals with strong activity, will be able to perceive and differentiate the exchange of healing life energy occurring between the two of them; they will be able to recognize both the existence and the exchange of healing life energy.

In a nutshell, healing life energy exchange refers to the neurotransmissive exchange that occurs with another in Kiryo. This neurotransmissive exchange becomes a mutual awakening of healing nervous systems caused by the stimulation from healing life energy.

Incidentally, in the Kiryo Academy, palm-to-palm exchange is conducted in the feeling-as-you-are state and is the fundamental and original Kiryo exercise configuration.

(3) Types of Hand Feedback Sensations: The Existence of the Perceptive Differentiation Nerve

The first sensation I felt in my palm was the cool, blowing feeling I mentioned earlier. Since then, during Kiryo exercise and Kiryo healing, I have felt many different types of hand-feedback sensations in my palms.

For instance, in Kiryo healing, certain differences occur based on symptoms of the areas affected by injury and illness that are being healed. Depending on the symptoms at the affected area, one may feel numbness, pressure, heat, crackling, sizzling, and/or prickling. In the same way, during Kiryo exercise, and depending on the other person's healing life energy, various types of hand feedback sensations may be felt.

Please look at Figure 3 on page 38: "Types of Hand Feedback Sensations at a Glance".

This table documents the various words used by the many people that have experienced Kiryo through either Kiryo exercise or Kiryo healing over the last twenty years. Every one of these people was mystified by the fact that they could feel in the palm of their hand something that they could not see. By the way, the "ball-like" feeling mentioned here refers to a feeling similar to holding a ball of Ki in one's hand.

People feeling and experiencing Kiryo exercise and Kiryo healing for the first time are especially surprised. In particular, I have noticed that it is quite easy for people suffering from injury and illness to feel healing life energy. Though, it has become abundantly clear that the power to feel healing life energy is something possessed latently by all people.

Figure 3: Types of Hand Feedback Sensations at a Glance

Sensory Word	Onomatopoeic Words
Stiffness	oomph-oomph
Heat	fwoo-fwoo
Warmth	crackle-crackle
Numbness	twitch-twitch
Ball-like	sparkle-sparkle
Pressure	sizzle-sizzle
Compression	throb-throb
Contraction	wrinkle-wrinkle
Tactile	zuuuun
Lukewarm	thud-thud
Fuzziness	lubb-lubb
Tickling	achy-achy
Windy	burn-burn
Stroking	pet-pet
Pulling	boing-boing
Weight	
Sunburn-like	
Cold	

If one performs Kiryo exercise while *feeling as they are*, they can quickly become able to feel the hand feedback sensation. All of us possess within us the perceptive differentiation nerve, and this nerve can easily be awakened and heightened by *feeling as one is*.

(4) The Hand Feedback Sensation Awakens the Primitive Brainstem

It is important to note that all the words listed in Figure 3, the "Types of Hand Feedback Sensations at a Glance", are very normal, common words. Consequently, there is something we have overlooked; things very important to humans and humanity can be hidden in expressions using sensory words and onomatopoeia.

The world of energy, in other words, is the world of healing power (healing life energy). Healing power specifically refers to the power to heal oneself and others. These healing powers allow us to defeat illness and prevent its future occurrence.

Please take another look at Figure 1 on page 22, "The Healing Sensory Function Forgotten by Humans". This chart is designed to help us decide whether to approach the world of Ki from the cognitive world or the sensory. That is, should we approach it through cognitive activity ordered by the cerebrum, or life activity ordered by the brainstem?

I believe that understanding the world of energy is extremely difficult. Though by first deciding as to whether we ought to approach it from either the cognitive or the sensory side, the task becomes easier to tackle.

4. The Activity and Role of the Sensory Stiffening Nerve

The sensory stiffening nerve is a part of the Kiryo nervous system. Specifically, the sensory stiffening nerve is the nerve which, independent of one's conscious will, adjusts the muscles (of the skeleton and the organs, etc.) in response to healing life energy exchange. This is the Kiryo nerve that has

39

concrete and direct effects on the body during Kiryo exercise and Kiryo healing.

Over the past twenty-odd years, countless phenomena and effects caused by Kiryo exercise and Kiryo healing have been observed. The unification of these results with the knowledge of modern medicine is what led to the discovery of the sensory stiffening nerve. I will now continue our discussion on the foundation of that premise.

(1) Even When Carrying out Life Energy Exchange with a Rhinoceros, My Hand Formed a Fist

On February 14th, 2007, an incident occurred in a classroom of the Osaka branch of the Kiryo Academy. A man in his fifties was attending a Kiryo exercise class. At first, he and I paired up and began to perform paired-healing-life energy exchange through our ku-no-ji palms.

Almost immediately after we began, his palm, arm, and entire body tensed up, and his face became red. Both of his ku-no-ji palms balled into tightly clenched fists and his whole body entered a stiffened state. His arms were slightly trembling. This man entered this same stiffened state whenever he practiced healing life-energy exchange with the other Kiryo Academy students as well.

As I looked at his clenched fist, memory of an incident suddenly came to mind. During the early years of my amateur era, I was performing Kiryo healing upon a recipient that had a strong healing response. My right ku-no-ji palm similarly clenched into a fist.

I remember how one young female patient, who was 26 at the time and suffered severe depression, suddenly entered into a severe convulsive fit, and her gentle face twisted into a near-demonic grimace. At the same time, the ku-no-ji palm through which I was sending the healing life-energy suddenly turned into a fist and stayed that way for about an hour.

Once her violent movements stopped, my right hand returned from a fist to the normal ku-no-ji form. The severe depression that girl had been suffering for eight years was cured in that single session.

Kiryo Exercise

The same muscular stiffening phenomenon caused the girl to undergo such violent spasms, and my hand to form a fist. Both my hand's shape and the girl's movements are examples of healing stiffness.

An excellent example of the forming of my palm into a fist happened in Kenya, Africa, when I engaged in Ki exchange with a rhinoceros.

In preparation for Ki exchange with the rhinoceros, which was about ten meters away from me, I held my right ku-no-ji palm at about elbow height. I then began the Ki exchange. Suddenly, I felt some sort of strong impact in my right ku no ji palm. My hand became a fist, and I wondered to myself, "What is going on?"

In truth, this occurred because the body life energy of the rhinoceros was far too strong, and as it fiercely stimulated the sensory stiffening nerve of my ku-no-ji palm, it forced my hand into a fist.

(2) Discovery and Naming of the Sensory Stiffening Nerve

I pondered many questions at this time. Why did I not notice my hands stiffening? What does this stiffening phenomenon mean? Is it an effect

41

of something else? What sort of effects does it, in turn, bring about?

One day, as I considered these mysteries, I arrived at the following thought: "What about the hands of my students?" That day, I went around softly touching the hands of my students as they practiced healing life-energy exchange in the classrooms of the academy.

Upon doing so, I noticed that, save for a few of them, almost all of the students' hands had become stiffly locked in the ku-no-ji palm. To their surprise, these students were not consciously aware of the fact that their hands had stiffened. They only took notice when I pointed it out to them, by touching their hands, that they had stiffly locked into the ku-no-ji palm.

What did this all mean? I was deep in thought when I realized something: perhaps, even though it is invisible, healing life-energy can act as an extrinsic stimulus.

For example, if we prick our skin with a needle, we feel the sharp sensation of being stung, and the muscles instantaneously stiffen. Similarly, when we touch something hot with our skin, our muscles spontaneously contract and stiffen. While these are physical phenomena, I could not help but think that healing life-energy was also stimulating the muscles in a similar manner.

Many forms of Ki Healing exercises are practiced at the academy but never has a student noticed that their hands had stiffened in the ku-no-ji form during healing life-energy exchange. It's no wonder I didn't notice this phenomenon in my own hands for over 20 years. I can now say that this stiffening is caused by orders issued by our brainstem.

Since that time, I began to think that this stiffness—muscular stiffness—was some sort of muscular adjustment. Thus, I began to review all the various past occurrences of sensory stiffening phenomenon.

As a general example, it is common during Kiryo healing for the fingers, arms, legs, or body of the Kiryo recipient (individual receiving Ki) to unconsciously move. People with chronic diseases, in particular, will move quite a lot. And when I ask the recipient about their movements, they are almost never aware of it.

If their movements are significant, some people may notice, but if the movements are subtle, nearly no one notices. These Ki recipients take notice for the first time once they're told that their hands and arms are moving. It has been this way for a long time.

I will explain the details in the next section, but I have concluded that these movements and this stiffening of the muscles caused by healing life-energy exchange happen involuntarily and are a wonderful healing form of muscular adjustment. The Kiryo nervous system orchestrates this muscular adjustment.

The occurrences with the fists helped attune me to the idea of sensory stiffness and showed me that this sensory stiffness is what causes healing muscular adjustment. That is how I discovered and decided to name the nerve that causes all of this: the sensory stiffening nerve.

(3) The Principle of Muscular Contraction and Relaxation

What are the structures and activities of human muscles?

Muscles come in three types: skeletal muscles, cardiac (heart) muscles, and visceral (organ) muscles.

The skeletal muscles are attached to the bones and are responsible for supporting the bone framework and moving the body. Skeletal muscles are striated muscles[7], in that they can be moved with our intentions, as they are voluntary muscles. Cardiac muscles form the walls of the heart and allow it to perform its pumping action.

Cardiac muscle is striated muscle, yet it is controlled by the autonomic nervous system, and cannot be moved by a person's intention; it is, therefore, an involuntary muscle. Viscera and visceral muscles include the various organs inside the thoracic and abdominal cavities, and their walls are made of smooth muscle. Smooth muscle is also controlled by the autonomic nervous system, and is, therefore, an involuntary muscle that cannot be moved by a person's intention.

By performing their specific functions and tasks when directed to do so by the central and peripheral nervous systems, muscles help to preserve

---

[7]"striated muscle" is a medical term used to classify muscles. In general, voluntary muscles are arranged into stripes, or "striations." Involuntary muscles do not have striations, and are called "smooth muscle." The only exception is cardiac muscle, which is striated but involuntary.

life itself. Muscles have the ability to shrink (contract). Skeletal and visceral muscles repeat cycles of contraction and relaxation in order to carry out their functions. Cardiac muscles and blood vessels also contract and expand when carrying out their functions. Additionally, the contraction and relaxation of the muscles in the arms and legs causes both venous blood and lymphatic fluid to be pushed up and onward throughout the body.[8]

What exactly is the source of the energy that allows muscles to contract?

I found some information contained in a particular medical textbook about this idea and recognized it to be worthy of attention with regards to Kiryo.

The Muscles' Source of Energy

Energy is necessary for things, such as muscles, to move. After eating, the carbohydrates in our food are broken down into glucose by digestive enzymes. This glucose is absorbed by the small intestine, diffused into the blood, and is then carried to the muscles throughout the body.

Elsewhere, the oxygen that is taken up by the lungs diffuses into red blood cells which are sent throughout the body. Glucose taken up by the muscles reacts with the oxygen brought by red blood cells to produce carbon dioxide, and energy is a byproduct of this reaction. The muscles can then use this energy to contract. This is similar to how an internal combustion engine uses oxygen to combust fuel and produce movement.[9] In sum, nutrients and oxygen are essential sources of energy for the muscles.

Let us now focus on the relationship between the muscles and blood. The muscles of the body contract and relax. The ability of skeletal muscles to contract is what allows them to support the body. Without this ability, the body cannot be maintained. Additionally, without the ability to contract, the visceral muscles would not be able to sustain our lives.

---

[8] The movements of the muscles in the legs and arms (primarily the legs) are used by the body to literally "push" the blood in the veins towards the heart so it can be recirculated. The lymph is moved around the body in the same way.
[9] *Organization of the Body*, ed. Tooru Mori

The weakening of muscle contraction causes the weakening of muscle relaxation, and the weakening of muscular contraction and relaxation results in poor blood flow. If blood flow is poor, the muscles become oxygen-deficient which causes the contractile ability of the muscles to worsen further.

The oxygen carried by the blood reacts with nutrients in the blood (glucose) and changes into carbon dioxide; this produces energy. Muscles contract using this produced energy, and, at the same time, the carbon dioxide gas is exchanged for more oxygen. In Kiryo terminology, this is called *internal respiration*.

In Kiryo, internal respiration (cellular respiration) is emphasized over external respiration. Internal respiration will be explained in more detail later.

(4) The Role and Activity of the Sensory Stiffness Nerve: Instantaneous Stiffening Improves Circulation of the Blood and Lymph

In Kiryo healing and Kiryo exercise, when exchange of healing energy occurs, healing life-energy stimulates and awakens the Kiryo nerves. At the same time, the perceptive differentiation nerve is awakened, and the brainstem receives this stimulus. The brainstem is then vitalized, and it sends strong life-sustaining orders to the sensory stiffness nerve.

The sensory stiffening nerve activates alongside the perceptive differentiation nerve. Upon receiving the stimulus of healing life energy, the sensory stiffening nerve instantaneously transmits stiffening contractions to the muscles. These continuous and instantaneous stiffening contractions allow muscles that have lost some of their contractile ability to regain it.

To explain the concept visually, when one *expands* the diminished contractional breadth of a muscle. Then, due to recoil from this expanded contraction, the breadth of the relaxation movement also increases. Thus, the breadth of both contraction and relaxation is increased and the muscles are adjusted to become softer and suppler. This causes blood circulation to become good and proper.

As healing life-energy exchange continues, with every passing instant,

45

stiffening contractions occur. This continuous stiffening contraction is referred to as *sustained instantaneous stiffening*. For those with low energy or a weak life force, or those suffering from chronic illness, sustained instantaneous stiffening is truly an uplifting experience that recharges their life.

Next, I will be explaining *sustained instantaneous contraction* in an easy-to-understand way. Please take a look at Figure 4, "A Pictorial Representation of Stiffening Contractions and Relaxations in the Muscles."

Figure 4: A Pictorial Representation of Stiffening Contractions and Relaxations in the Muscles

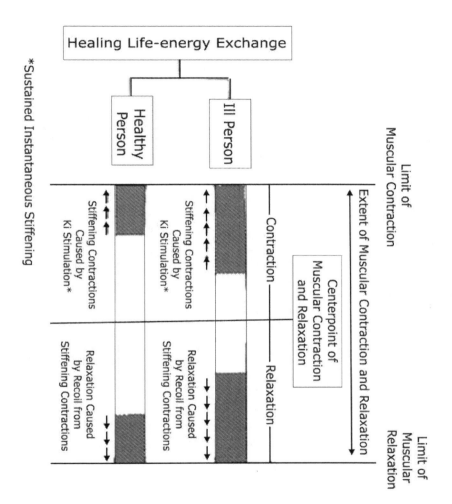

47

This diagram is an internal depiction of the contraction and relaxation of the muscles. The first thing it depicts is the extent of the muscles' contraction and relaxation. To depict the limits of these processes, I have used a line on the left edge to indicate the limit of contraction, and a line on the right edge to indicate the limit of relaxation. Right in the middle of these two lines, I have drawn a line representing the center point between contraction and relaxation. The region to the left of this line is the extent of contraction, and the region to the right is the extent of relaxation.

Please look at the portion of the figure that compares the contractions of an ill person to that of a healthy person. The white, contractile space for the ill person is depicted as one-third of the size of the total possible contraction, while the contractile space for the healthy person is depicted as two-thirds of the total possible contraction. The relaxation space for each individual is similarly divided.

When the contractions and relaxations of the muscles are small and weak, circulation of blood and lymph is poor. In people that suffer from chronic diseases, weak contraction and relaxation causes especially poor circulation of the blood and lymphatic fluid. When blood circulation is poor, nutrients (glucose) and oxygen are lacking. These individuals are in a state of poor circulation where muscular and blood flow adjustments are absent. Healthy individuals are in a state of good circulation where muscular and blood flow adjustments are present.

Next, compare the diagonally-shaded parts of the sick person diagram and the healthy person diagram. The image shows that for sick persons, one third of the total width of contraction is white, while for healthy persons, two thirds of the total width is white. This is a central point to understand.

Healing life-energy exchange will cause both ill and healthy people to be stimulated by Ki (healing life energy). Instantly and simultaneously, their sensory stiffening nerves will activate and begin working. As a result, their muscles will begin to contract and stiffen instantly: both the ill and healthy person's muscles are, in their own way, repeating contraction and relaxation.

The sensory stiffening nerve causes a normally contracting muscle to further and instantaneously contract (shrink) and stiffen; this fosters a strong contractile ability. The recoil from this motion will cause the muscles to relax (loosen). Once Ki (healing life energy) exchange begins, the instantaneous stiffening of the muscles also begins to continuously occur.

The longer you continue this healing life-energy exchange, the more the contractile ability of the muscles will increase, and the diagonally-shaded portion of the contraction column in Figure 4 will grow smaller. Consequently, the white part of the contraction column will grow larger, and your normal contractile range will widen.

When the contractions and relaxations of the muscles grow larger, the muscles become softer. In Kiryo, this effect, brought about by sustained instantaneous contraction, is called muscular adjustment. Muscular adjustment amplifies the recovery power of an ill person, and also contributes to the prevention of illness in a healthy individual.

By the way, in terms of the nervous activity related to muscular contraction and relaxation, the function of the autonomic nervous system is homeostatic maintenance of muscular contraction and relaxation. Likewise, the function of the motor nervous system is to contract and relax (extend) the muscles for motor activity. The function of the sensory stiffening nerve is to achieve instantaneous stiffening contraction and relaxation as a healing sensory function in the muscles.

The autonomic nervous contraction and relaxation of the muscles and the sensory stiffening nerve's instantaneous stiffening contraction and relaxation (sustained instantaneous stiffening) of the muscles work together to adjust the visceral and skeletal muscles to become softer. Few people are aware of sustained instantaneous stiffening of the muscles caused by the sensory stiffening nerve, let us make as much use of it as we can.

Note: Muscular contraction and relaxation also creates an internal massage-like effect upon the scalp and skin, which is why I also believe it to be quite good for beauty as well.

(5) The Sensory Stiffening Nerve is the Cornerstone of Kiryo and Modern Medicine

The sensory stiffening nerve is an important cornerstone that unifies the Kiryo nervous system and the modern medical nervous system. The sensory stiffening nerve is simultaneously activated with the Kiryo nerve and the perceptive differentiation nerve by Kiryo exercise and Kiryo healing, and together these three work to awaken the primitive brainstem.

49

The awakened primitive brainstem unifies with the modern brainstem to create the wholesome brainstem. This wholesome brainstem sends powerful orders to keep living to the Kiryo and modern medical nervous systems.

The wholesome brainstem heightens symbiotic healing power. Further, if there is a part of the body affected by illness or injury, it heals it. If one is healthy, it protects against future illness.

The sensory stiffening nerve specifically and directly brings about Kiryo healing effects inside the body. This is because the sensory stiffening nerve works in concert with the autonomic nervous system of modern medicine to bring about the Kiryo effects of recovery and restoration. The sensory stiffening nerve is the cornerstone of the unified effects of the nerves that seek to bring about healing. The unified effects of these nerves bring about seven adjustments of body and mind, which I will discuss in the next section.

The seven healing adjustments of mind and body are: muscular adjustment, blood flow adjustment, respiratory adjustment, immune adjustment, hormonal adjustment, body temperature adjustment, and mental adjustment.

5. The Unified Effects of the Kiryo Nervous System and the Modern Medical Nervous System

When the Kiryo nervous system and the modern medical nervous system are unified, the seven healing adjustments of mind and body occur—muscular adjustment, blood flow adjustment, respiratory adjustment, immune adjustment, hormonal adjustment, body temperature adjustment, and mental adjustment. These healing adjustments of body and mind further amplify the symbiotic healing powers.

The natural healing power that drives the natural, gradual healing of illnesses and injuries takes time to achieve its effects. In contrast, the aforementioned healing adjustments of body and mind greatly amplify the symbiotic healing powers which proactively heal and cure illness and injury.

Our bodies possess not only the power to heal ourselves, but also the power to heal other people or animals, which is the other healing power.

In this next section, I will examine in detail just how the unified effects of the Kiryo nervous system and the modern medical nervous system are brought about.

(1) The Relationship Between the Primitive Brainstem and the Kiryo Nerve: The Kiryo Nervous System

Let us conceptually discuss exactly how the Kiryo nervous system functions in response to the healing life-energy exchange (neurotransmissive exchange) that occurs during Kiryo exercise and Kiryo healing.

First, take a look at Figure 5 on page 52, "Diagram of the Relationship between the Primitive Brainstem and the Kiryo Nervous System". I will explain this diagram now, focusing on the Kiryo nerves.

When healing life energy exchange (neurotransmissive exchange) occurs, first, the Kiryo nerve is activated. The activated Kiryo nerve awakens the primitive brainstem that lies dormant in the modern brainstem. This primitive brainstem has lived on inside our modern brainstems since primordial times as genetic information.

As I explained previously, our modern brainstems are currently weakening, and our cerebra are strengthening. The primitive brainstem, awakened by healing life-energy exchange, unifies with the modern brainstem and vitalizes it. The two then become the wholesome brainstem, which sends strong orders to keep living to the modern medical nervous system, and also to the Kiryo nervous system.

The wholesome brainstem unifies the Kiryo nerves and the modern medical nerves into one entity, and in doing so, manifests strong recovery/restoration effects upon illness and injury.

Additionally, the Kiryo nerve sends orders of perception and differentiation to the perceptive differentiation nerve, and at the same time, sends orders of instantaneous muscular stiffening to the sensory stiffening nerve.

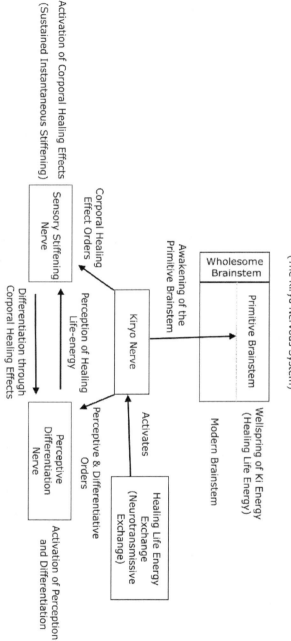

Figure 5: Diagram of the Relationship between the
Primitive Brainstem and the Kiryo Nervous System

(The Kiryo Nervous System)

52

Please once again look at Figure 5, "Diagram of the Relationship Between the Primitive Brain and the Kiryo Nerves". A great deal of information can be gleaned from this diagram which I will now explain. Please ensure that you have understood the overall structure of the figure.

1.   The Primitive Brainstem and Kiryo Nerves are Abstract Entities

The primitive brain lies dormant in our current brainstems. It is awakened by its peripheral nerves, the Kiryo nerves.

Both the primitive brainstem and the Kiryo nerves are abstract, conceptual objects. This abstractness may make them difficult to understand, but in Kiryo theory they perform an indispensable, crucial, and all-encompassing function in the operation of the system as a whole.

2.   The Perceptive Differentiation and Sensory Stiffening Nerves are Concrete Entities

Compared to the abstract nature of the primitive brainstem and the Kiryo nerves, the perceptive differentiation and sensory stiffening nerves manifest concrete healing effects in our bodies. In particular, the sensory stiffening nerve brings about various different observable healing effects upon the body.

At this point, we're in need of a term to collectively refer to these observable healing effects. In Kiryo terminology, these effects are referred to as *corporal healing effects*. Corporal healing effects are the real, observable healing effects brought about in the human body by the action of the sensory stiffening nerve. In accordance with this diagram, we can divide the duties of the corporal healing effects into two main subcategories.

(3) The Relationship Between the Perceptive Differentiation Nerve and the Sensory Stiffening Nerve: Heightening of Perception and Differentiation

Exchange of healing life-energy (neurotransmissive exchange) activates the Kiryo nerves, which then transmit perception and differentiation commands to the perceptive differentiation nerves. These nerves transmit this perceived healing life-energy to the sensory stiffening nerve.

Simultaneously, the Kiryo nerves transmit corporal healing commands to the sensory stiffening nerve. The sensory stiffening nerve receives these commands from both the Kiryo nerves and the perceptive differentiation nerve. It then causes sustained instantaneous stiffening of the body's muscles, which is a manifestation of corporal healing effects.

Sustained instantaneous stiffening of the body's muscles creates stiffness and rigidity in the palm of the ku-no-ji palm, the sole of the foot, and throughout the body itself. This stiffness and rigidity imparts differentiative ability to the perceptive differentiation nerve, enabling it to differentiate changes in healing life energy.

(2) The Unified Effects of the Kiryo Nervous System and the Modern Medical Nervous System

I have already discussed the relationship between the Kiryo nervous system and the nervous system of modern medicine. Yet another function of the sensory stiffening nerve is to unify these two nervous systems. The sensory stiffening nerve is the keystone to the manifestation of the unified effects of the Kiryo and modern medical nervous systems; it forms and functions as the node that connects these two.

Once these two nervous systems are unified, the three healing adjustments (the three adjustments principle) and the healing adjustment of mind and body are manifested as corporal healing effects. The three adjustments principle (discussed soon) and the healing adjustment of mind and body are what heal injuries and illnesses. They heighten the symbiotic healing powers, leading to the enhancement of health itself.

Please refer to Figure 6 on page 56: "The Unified Effects of the Kiryo Nervous System and the Modern Medical Nervous System." I will now explain the information contained therein.

First, the "brainstem", bounded by the double-lined box, refers to our current brainstem. I have written the "primitive brainstem" horizontally above this, bounded with a single-line box, and made it slightly bigger for emphasis. The primitive brainstem is the portion of our brain that originates in ancient history. It has been recorded and transmitted down to us through our genes and lies dormant in our current brainstems.

The primitive brainstem survived the harsh, cruel circumstances of the primordial era of its birth and has since been passed down till the present, where it now lies dormant inside us. The primitive brainstem is the more resilient brainstem. It is also the source of healing power (healing life energy).

When the primitive and modern brainstems unify, they form the *wholesome brainstem*. Next, the wholesome brainstem, using the sensory stiffening nerve as its mechanism, brings about the unification of the Kiryo nervous system and the modern medical nervous system. Once these two systems have fused, the healing adjustment of mind and body is manifested as a corporal healing effect.

Muscular adjustment is the adjustment of muscle cells; blood flow adjustment adjusts the heart and the vasculature (the blood vessels), providing them with nutrients and oxygen. Respiratory adjustment causes adjustment of internal respiration (internal gas exchange); immune adjustment adjusts the lymph; hormonal adjustment interacts with individual hormones; body temperature adjustment results in elevation of core body temperature; adjustment of the mind stabilizes the spirit and psyche. It is in this way that "healing adjustment of the mind and body" is carried out.

Figure 6: The Unified Effects of the Kiryo Nervous System and the Modern Medical Nervous System

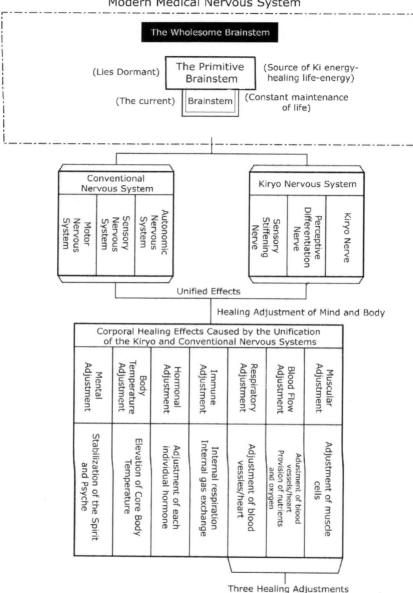

Three Healing Adjustments
(Three Adjustments Principle)

(3) The Three Healing Adjustments Simultaneously Carry Out Corporal Healing Effects

As the manifestations of the corporal healing effects caused by the sensory stiffening nerve, the following three adjustments are carried out simultaneously: muscular adjustment, blood flow adjustment, and respiratory adjustment. These three healing adjustments are known as the "three healing adjustments" or the "three adjustments principle."

Please refer to Figure 7 on page 58: "Diagram of the Relationship Between the Three Healing Adjustments." These three healing adjustments instantaneously stimulate the activity of the sensory stiffening nerve through neurotransmissive exchange (healing life energy exchange). This function enables the three healing adjustments to simultaneously bring about corporal healing effects. With regards to muscular adjustment, blood flow adjustment, and respiratory adjustment, I will discuss their effects on each other (as designated by (A) through (F) in the diagram).

(A) *Muscular Adjustment Upon Blood Flow Adjustment*

As neurotransmissive exchange begins, the sensory stiffening nerve begins to work. This nerve activity changes the movements of the muscles (skeletal and visceral) from contraction and relaxation to instantaneous stiffening contractions and relaxations.

Sustained instantaneous stiffening contractions and relaxations cause the muscles to need more energy, and therefore more blood: this activity strongly stimulates blood flow. The increased blood flow makes the normal contractions and relaxations of the muscles more vigorous, and the muscles are then adjusted to be more soft and supple.

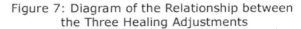

Figure 7: Diagram of the Relationship between
the Three Healing Adjustments

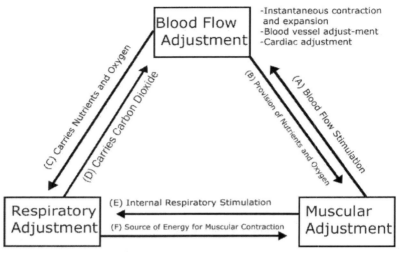

※ In Kiryo exercise and Kiryo healing, the three healing adjustments—
muscular, blood flow, and respiratory adjustment—brought about by the
exchange of healing life energy occur simultaneously.

※ Muscular adjustment is the adjustment of muscle cells.

(B) Blood Flow Adjustment Upon Muscular Adjustment

Blood flow adjustment primarily involves adjustment of the blood vessels (cardiac adjustment). Blood vessel adjustment and cardiac adjustment are coupled with instantaneous stiffening contractions and relaxations of the muscles. This coupling enables the blood vessels to change from contraction and expansion to instantaneous contraction and expansion.

When the muscles are stiff, the blood vessels are contracted. When the muscles are relaxed, the blood vessels are more expanded.

Blood vessel adjustment is also coupled with muscular adjustment. Just as the muscles become softer and suppler, the blood vessels become softer and wider. Additionally, as the contractions and expansions of the blood vessels become more pronounced, cardiac adjustments are carried out in a coupled manner and blood flow becomes healthy.

Good blood flow enables the provision of nutrients and oxygen to every corner of the body. It also allows for more efficient removal of waste products as well as the improvement of regenerative metabolism.[10]

(C) Blood Flow Adjustment Upon Respiratory Adjustment

Nutrients and oxygen are carried by blood flow throughout the body. Nutrients are transformed by digestive enzymes into glucose, which is carried throughout the body, including to skeletal and visceral muscles, as well as to other types of muscle, where it diffuses into them.

At the same time, oxygen permeates into the bloodstream and is carried throughout the body. The glucose that has permeated into the muscles reacts with the oxygen brought there by red blood cells and changes into carbon dioxide.

---

[10]Regenerative Metabolism - Unfortunately, Kanzawa doesn't give much explanation for this term beyond what has been translated. It appears to be a term he's made up, as I can't find any other record of it. "Metabolism" can mean "turnover" as in "turnover of old cells for new ones." Thus, "regenerative metabolism" is basically "regenerative cellular turnover."

Put simply, glucose and oxygen react, carbon dioxide is produced, and energy is released as a byproduct. This is the oxygen and carbon dioxide gas exchange process; it is also referred to as internal respiration or cellular respiration. Because internal respiration is carried out at the level of each individual cell, in Kiryo, it gained the name cellular respiration.

Adjustment of this cellular process is referred to as respiratory adjustment. Kiryo can easily improve one's internal respiration. In fact, this improvement is a very important part of Kiryo.

(D) Respiratory Adjustment Upon Blood Flow Adjustment

The carbon dioxide generated by internal respiration is carried to the lungs by the blood, and the lungs then expel it outside the body. The internal respiration of Kiryo is based in the body's natural respiratory processes. If internal respiration is improved, then external respiration will also improve.

(E) Muscular Adjustment Upon Respiratory Adjustment

The contractions and relaxations of our muscles can be divided into two types based on the activity of the nerves that cause them. One type is the contraction and relaxation of the skeletal muscles powered by the motor nervous system.

The skeletal muscles are usually just called muscles. Normally, we use our cerebrum and motor nervous system to contract and relax these muscles and move our body. Voluntarily contracting and relaxing our skeletal muscles comes naturally to us and so moving our arms, legs, and body requires little to no thought.[11]

The other type of muscular contraction and relaxation is carried out by the autonomic nervous system. These sorts of contractions and relaxations are performed by the autonomic nervous system and our

---

[11] Saying contraction and extension may be easier for some to understand than contraction and relaxation.

60

brainstem to preserve life and maintain health. In this case, the skeletal muscles do not receive commands from the cerebrum and the motor nervous system, but from the brainstem and the autonomic nervous system. The skeletal muscles are voluntary muscles that can be controlled by the cerebrum and the motor nervous system. They are at the same time involuntary muscles that are controlled by the cerebellum and autonomic nervous system.

Kiryo focuses on the involuntary muscular contractions and relaxations that are carried out by the cerebellum and autonomic nervous system to preserve life and maintain health. Kiryo unifies this autonomic system with the sensory stiffening nerve, and as an effect of this unification, makes the contractions and relaxations it produces more pronounced. The unified effects of these two nerves causes a corporal healing effect as the contractions and relaxations of the muscles become instantaneous stiffening contractions and relaxations. In Kiryo, this is known as muscular adjustment carried out by sustained instantaneous stiffening.

This muscular adjustment greatly stimulates internal respiration. Internal respiration is the gas exchange between oxygen and carbon dioxide that occurs inside the body. Internal respiration brought about by muscular adjustment is called respiratory adjustment cellular respiration.

When we speak of respiration or breathing, we usually are referring to the process of sucking in and blowing out air through the nose or mouth, a process that takes place outside the body. I, myself, thought the same in the past. However, in truth, the primary goal of respiration is not external respiration but internal respiration.

If internal respiration is improved, the breathing muscles become softer and more responsive, and external breathing is naturally improved. Thus, muscular adjustment stimulates both blood flow and internal respiration.

(F) Respiratory Adjustment Upon Muscular Adjustment

Muscular adjustment changes the contractions and relaxations of the muscles into instantaneous stiffening contractions and relaxations. These instantaneous stiffening contractions require more oxygen than typical contractions do.

61

Oxygen reacting with glucose and transforming into carbon dioxide and resulting in energy being produced, is the internal respiration, or cellular respiration, that respiratory adjustment acts upon.

Respiratory adjustment brings about healing energy exchange that simultaneously causes both muscular and blood flow adjustment. Simply put, respiratory adjustment, by way of the oxygen and carbon dioxide gas-exchange process, creates a robust energy source. The muscles, having undergone muscular adjustment and changed their contractions to instantaneous stiffening contractions, require this energy source to sustain these contractions.

Above, I have described the relationship between the three healing adjustments: muscular adjustment, blood flow adjustment, and respiratory adjustment. These three healing adjustments form the core of Kiryo theory and are also the *healing principle*. From this point on, I'll be collectively referring to these three healing adjustments as the *three adjustments principle*. Next, I'll be using the *three adjustments principle* as a foundation for the discussion of the healing adjustment of mind and body.

(4) Healing Adjustment of Body and Mind is Facilitated by the Unified Effects of the Modern Medical and Kiryo Nervous Systems

Before I can discuss the adjustment of mind and body resulting from corporal healing effects, I would like to consider the issue of the *effects of Kiryo*; a problem whose solution eluded me for many years.

When I speak of the effects of Kiryo, I am referring to both the healing life-energy-mediated recovery from injury and illness as well as the soothing and dulling of pain. Indeed, recovery and the dulling of pain are two sides of the same coin. As an effect of Kiryo exercise and Kiryo healing, injury and illness is healed, and the pain those ailments bring about is alleviated.

But why exactly do these wonderful Kiryo effects, brought about by the exchange of healing life-energy (neurotransmissive exchange), occur? This critical question remained a mystery to me for many years. Though I don't consider myself an expert in medical science, I had long thought that there was some unknown "life defense system" inside our bodies that protects us from illness. I theorized that Kiryo could form the proof for the existence of this inexplicable force inside the body.

I then began to consider, from the standpoint of Kiryo, the accepted, widely-known truths of conventional medicine. I paid special attention to the nervous system as detailed by modern medicine, and eventually discovered—empirically, through Kiryo practice—its unified (joint) action with the Kiryo nervous system. I learned that the activity of the Kiryo nervous system causes improvement in one's self-healing and partner-healing ability, which invigorates the manifestation of Kiryo effects.

The healing adjustment of mind and body, carried out as a unified effect of the Kiryo and conventional nervous systems, is a manifestation of corporal healing effects. This adjustment of mind and body heals injuries and illnesses and alleviates pain; it is the manifestation of the effects of Kiryo itself. I would like to hypothetically derive these Kiryo effects in the context of the characteristic elements of the Kiryo field.

Please take another look at Figure 6 on page 56: "The Unified Effects of the Kiryo Nervous System and the Modern Medical Nervous System."

Starting from the top, we have the wholesome brainstem. The exchange of healing energy that takes place in Kiryo exercise and Kiryo healing awakens the primitive brainstem which lies dormant within the current brainstem. The awakened primitive brainstem unifies with the current brainstem, transforming it into the wholesome brainstem.

Next, as the wholesome brainstem sends commands to both the Kiryo nervous system and the modern brainstem, it also sends unified affect commands to both. These unified affect commands cause the Kiryo nervous system and the conventional nervous system to unify with each other. The sensory stiffening nerve plays the role of a keystone in the unification of these two nervous systems. It and the autonomic nervous system are what proactively bring about this unification.

To be precise, the sensory stiffening nerve and the autonomic nervous systems (sympathetic and parasympathetic nerves) work in concert with each other to bring about this unification. The three healing adjustments I discussed earlier also work together with the autonomic nervous system. The activity of the autonomic nervous system is vital to human life.

63

Next, we see that the healing adjustment of mind and body is brought about as a corporal healing effect manifested by the unified action of the Kiryo and modern medical nervous systems. The healing of mind is primarily due to the activity of the sensory stiffening nerve and the autonomic nervous system. The autonomic nervous system assumes the leading role and the sensory stiffening nerve works behind it. Let us now break down the healing adjustment of body and mind.

1. Contemplating Why Kiryo Effects Work on Injury and Illness at the Muscular Level

Why does healing life-energy cause Kiryo effects like the healing of injury and illness or the alleviation/dulling of pain? Here I will illuminate this mystery from an empirical perspective.

How exactly are structures like our skeletal and visceral muscles working? As I have explained earlier, the muscles continuously repeat cycles of contraction and relaxation. The contractions and relaxations of the muscles are the energy (foundation) required for the absorption of nutrients and removal of waste products that takes place in regenerative metabolism.

So then, let us contemplate, at the level of the muscle cell, why exactly Kiryo effects (recovery and restoration/dulling of pain) exist.

2. Instantaneous Stiffening Contractions of Skeletal Muscles Improve Regenerative Metabolism

Kiryo acts primarily and most importantly upon the contractions and relaxations of the skeletal muscles that are responsible for the maintenance of life. This is because the contraction and relaxation of the skeletal muscles causes the blood to flow, enabling the absorption of nutrients and oxygen and expulsion of waste products: processes essential for regenerative metabolism. Kiryo causes the contraction and relaxation of the skeletal muscles to change to sustained instantaneous stiffening contractions and relaxations, enabling them to improve regenerative metabolism.

Sustained instantaneous stiffening contractions and relaxations stimulate blood flow and have the ability to cause speedy, abundant provision of nutrients and oxygen to muscle cells, as well as speedy removal of waste products. In other words, they have the power to cause rapid regenerative metabolism at the level of the skeletal muscle cell.

I believe what enables the recovery from illness, and the dulling of pain, is the rapid regenerative metabolism of skeletal muscle cells. I will now present an illustrative case of this in action.

Case: My Wife's Injury of Her Left Ribs

This story takes place back when I was an amateur in Kiryo healing, newly awakened to Ki energy. A time when my wife regarded my daily Kiryo healing practice with cold, distrusting eyes.

One morning, my wife, was inside the bathroom, cleaning it. Suddenly, the mat on the floor slipped against the tile, and she lost her footing. Her weight fell against the edge of the bathtub, and it struck her forcefully on her left ribs. Barely able to bear the pain, she made her way to me as I was sleeping in my bed. In a half-awake daze, I placed, without much thought, my right hand—in the ku-no-ji shape—against her left ribs, and began to send (exchange) Ki (healing life energy) into the affected area.

Immediately, my wife cried out in pain, but I continued the Ki exchange regardless. About a minute passed, and I then asked my wife how she felt. She replied that she felt like the pain in her left ribs, which earlier was only spreading, had been "sucked up and away" into my right palm.

We both had to leave for work not long after, and thus I was only able to continue the Kiryo healing for about twelve minutes. Even so, her pain was only slight in the area she had struck against the tub, and the pain in the surrounding region was completely gone. I was as surprised as my wife.

Since that incident, my wife's cold regard of my work stopped, and she began to recognize the power of Kiryo.

Why was my Kiryo healing able to dull my wife's rib pain and recover and restore her injured self?

65

To answer this, let us divide the skeletal muscles into differently colored groups and consider each. We will call these the *muscular color zones*. An explanation of each muscular color zone follows.

○ Muscular Color Zones (Muscle Cell Color Zones)

- White Zone

  ➤ The white zone contains muscles (muscle cells) that are functioning normally.

- Black Zone (Abnormal Muscle Cells)

  ➤ The black zone contains muscles (muscle cells) of a part of the body affected by injury or illness, and as such are functioning abnormally.

- Gray Zone (Quasi-Abnormal Muscle Cells)

  ➤ The gray zone contains muscles (muscle cells) that have reached a state of quasi-abnormality due to the influence of a part of the body affected by injury or illness. The degree and extent of abnormality in the affected part in turn affects the extent of the gray zone.

Based on the severity of the condition affecting the ill or injured area, the black zone cells around it become darker, and in turn, the gray zone cells around those cells spread and become darker themselves. On the contrary, if the affected, black zone disappears, the gray zone surrounding it does as well. When the black and grey zones disappear, the cells in the area return to their normal, white zone state. In other words, they become healthy. Important to note, the muscular color zone groups apply to and can describe visceral muscles just as they do to skeletal muscles.

Let us now use our knowledge of color zones at the muscle cell level to examine why exactly, in the case of my wife, the Kiryo effects of dulling of pain and recovery and restoration from illness were manifested.

Why did the pain in my wife's left ribs, the area she struck against the bathtub, disappear so quickly? That mystery can be solved if we consider the muscles involved at the cellular level.

66

Muscles are comprised of individual, micron-sized muscle cells. Countless numbers of these cells together make up one muscle. When my wife struck her muscles against the tub, the muscles in the area became inflamed, causing pain. Inflammation is a bodily process that occurs in response to bacterial infection or chemical and physical factors, and it involves reddening, swelling, throbbing pain, and production of heat in a portion of the body.

In the case of my wife, the physical action of striking her left ribs against the tub created throbbing pain in her side. That part of her body struck (the affected part), and the area around it became inflamed. Then, unable to bear the pain caused by this, she cried out.

What sort of changes occurred in the state of the muscle cells in and around the struck region?

The cells of the struck part (the affected part) ceased their normal contractions and relaxations, and blood flow to the region was almost completely restricted; these cells, therefore, fell victim to a critical lapse in oxygen. As a result, they triggered severe pain.

The area surrounding the struck region was similarly affected. The normal contractions and relaxations of the cells in the surrounding region were weakened, and blood flow to this region worsened. The inflammation in the struck region spread also to the cells surrounding it, and these cells then also experienced a critical lack of oxygen; this resulted in the pain spreading outwards, beyond the acutely affected region.

Given all this, why was my Kiryo healing able to remove and heal the severe pain in my wife's ribs? The answer is that healing life-energy, invisible to my eyes, passed through my five-fingered ku no ji (right) hand, and stimulated the nerves (Kiryo nervous system) in my wife's ailing part (the part she hit on the tub). This stimulation brought about the three adjustments principle (the three healing adjustments), which in turn recovered and restored the affected area.

The activation of the three adjustments principle brings about several effects. First, *sustained instantaneous stiffening contractions* are brought about via the adjustment of the muscles; simultaneously, severe pain increases.

67

Unable to bear this, my wife cried out. By the way, the sustained instantaneous stiffening contractions caused by the activity of the sensory stiffening nerve cause muscular adjustment rather forcibly. As a result, they may, at times, temporarily increase pain.

Applying what we know about color zones to the case of my wife's injury, we see that in the struck portion (black zone) and its surrounding area (gray zone), inflammation and pain were spreading as a result of the injury itself. As I began my Kiryo healing, there occurred almost simultaneously a stopping of the spread of the inflammation, and the extent of the spread of inflammation and pain in the gray zone shrunk considerably in the blink of an eye.

I believe this reduction in the size of the gray zone was brought about by the activity of the three adjustments principle. The sustained instantaneous stiffening contractions caused by muscular adjustment, the provision of oxygen caused by blood flow adjustment, and the cellular respiration caused by respiratory adjustment. The activity of these three adjustments caused the gray zone (inflamed area) to speedily change into a white zone (normal muscle cells). Additionally, the black zone (the struck portion) was changed into a gray zone, which then eventually transformed into the normal muscle cells of the white zone. My wife's left ribs which she struck on the bathtub were completely restored within two or three days.

In Kiryo, this sort of speedy recovery and restoration of illness and injury is referred to as "rapid muscle cell regenerative metabolism."

(3) Cellular Adjustment of the Viscera and Visceral Muscles: Sends Orders to Each Organ While Maintaining Balance with the Sympathetic Nervous System

The fundamentals of the contractions and relaxations of the viscera (visceral muscles) do not differ very much from those of the skeletal muscles, but in terms of the preservation of the processes of life, there is a very significant difference. The contractions and relaxations of the skeletal muscles facilitate the flow of blood and lymph—an important role, to be sure— but the viscera (and visceral muscles) each have different roles depending on what organ they are part of. Their contractions and relaxations are what enable them to perform this role.

The contractions and relaxations of the viscera and the visceral muscles can be said to be the activity of life itself. The autonomic nervous system is what directly controls (oversees) the contractions and relaxations of the viscera and visceral muscles.

The central component of the autonomic nervous system is the brainstem. As explained earlier, Kiryo unifies the primitive and current brainstems and fashions them into the wholesome brainstem. The wholesome brainstem unifies together the sensory stiffening nerve and the autonomic nervous system. These two nerves, together, directly control (oversee) the viscera and visceral muscles.

Because Kiryo centers itself around the wholesome brainstem, it naturally allows for the sending of wholesome orders to each organ while maintaining a balance between the sympathetic and parasympathetic nervous systems centered around the latter. At the same time, it sends orders along the sensory stiffening nerve to each organ.

Here, in order to further deepen our understanding of the contractions and relaxations of each visceral muscle, I'd like to go over once again the particulars thereof.

o Considering Uterine Myomas[12] from the Level of the Muscle Cell

Please take another look at Figure 4 on page 47: "Diagram of Stiffening Contractions and Relaxations of The Muscles." This figure depicts the extent of the contractions and relaxations of the muscles in a pictorial format.

The smaller the extent of these contractions and relaxations, and the closer the maximum extent of the contraction draws to the center line, the worse the contractions and relaxations are understood to be: this signifies that these contractions and relaxations are not normal. Let us examine this in the case of the uterus.

The myoma (uterine tumor) is the affected part, and therefore is the black zone. The area surrounding the myoma is the gray zone, and the rest of the muscles are in the white zone—normal muscles and muscle cells. Upon administering Kiryo healing to this uterine myoma, sustained

[12]"myoma" means muscle tumor.

instantaneous stiffening is observed.

Thus, the muscles of the uterus instantaneously stiffen and then relax. This occurs continuously. As a result, the contractions and relaxations of the white zone muscles and muscle cells become more normal, and even the contractions and relaxations of the gray zone muscle cells become normal, and these muscles and cells are regeneratively metabolized into normal muscles and cells. All we have left is the black zone.

Now comes a showdown between the white and black zones. The sustained instantaneous stiffening of the muscles slowly begins to make the contractions and relaxations of the muscles in the black zone normal, causing the uterine myoma to shrink. Eventually, the myoma either shrinks to a point that it cannot adversely affect the body anymore, or it completely vanishes. Of course, it is obvious that this change occurred as a result of the three healing adjustments (muscular, blood flow, and respiratory adjustment).

Let us now examine the muscular adjustments at play here from the perspective of the entire uterus itself.

When administering Kiryo healing (exchange of healing life energy) to the uterine myoma, there is something that must be confirmed. The Kiryo healing must be temporarily interrupted, and the Kiryo recipient, with their understanding, must be asked to place the palm of their hand lightly on the upper part of the uterus. Doing this will enable the recipient to feel the uterus undulating and moving in response to the treatment.

The Kiryo recipient will feel as though the uterus is undulating and moving in response to the light pressure I am applying with the palm of my hand. We will both, no doubt, be surprised upon feeling the movement of the uterus ourselves. In fact, this movement of the uterus is actually a manifestation of corporal healing effects brought about by the unification of the autonomic nervous system and sensory stiffening nerve.

This corporal healing effect refers to the changing of the contracting and relaxing movements of the uterus to instantaneous stiffening contracting and relaxing movements. These movements are the repeated instantaneous stiffening contractions and relaxations that are needed to shrink the uterine myoma.

Let us think of the uterus as a towel that has absorbed a great deal of water. The normal contractions and relaxations of the uterus (action of the autonomic nervous system) are light wringings of this towel, and the

70

instantaneous stiffening contractions and relaxations (action of the sensory stiffening nerve) are vigorous wringings.

Upon beginning Kiryo healing (exchange of healing life energy), sustained instantaneous stiffening manifests in the uterus as a corporal healing effect. This causes the "water-filled towel" of the uterus to no longer be only lightly wrung, but vigorously wrung.

The myoma and the surrounding tissue (the water in the towel) is twisted back and forth, and vigorously wrung out. These repeated vigorous wringings are what shrink the size of the myoma cells. Eventually, the myoma either shrinks to a point that it cannot adversely affect the body anymore, or it completely vanishes. Thus, the contractions and relaxations of the uterus return to normal, and it can resume its normal function.

This process can be applied to all internal organs, both at the micro (cellular) level and the macro (whole structure) level.

The Effects of Kiryo on Cancer

It is said that in the near future, one in two people will eventually suffer from some sort of cancer. Cancer, with its relapses and metastases, various forms and complications, is a very difficult disease.

Let us narrow down our focus to just the initial, primary incidence of cancer, and discuss the effects of Kiryo on such a disease. While cancer can affect a great many organs, including the stomach, the colon, the liver, and the bladder, we will consider in our coming discussions stomach cancer to be a representative example of the disease.

For the sake of this example, let us say that a particular individual has a 1 cm cancerous stomach tumor. This 1 cm tumor is the black zone. The area surrounding this black zone is the area in which the cancerous cells are trying to multiply and grow: the gray zone. The remaining area is the white zone: normal stomach muscle cells.

When Kiryo healing using the ku-no-ji palm begins, the contractions and relaxations of the muscles and muscle cells of the stomach change, through the application of sustained instantaneous stiffening, into instantaneous stiffening contractions and relaxations. These instantaneous stiffening contractions and relaxations become especially pronounced and robust in the white zone, causing the area to move.

The muscle cells in the gray zone are being converted into cancerous cells by the proliferative action of the tumor cells. However, sustained instantaneous stiffening causes normal contractions and relaxations in this tissue, which brings blood that provides nutrients and oxygen, enabling normal internal respiration (cellular respiration). Additionally, lymph is brought to this tissue, and the immune response is then heightened.

Finally, we have the *black-and-white* showdown of the black zone and the white zone. The cancer cells of the black zone slowly begin to resume their normal contractions and relaxations due to the action of sustained instantaneous stiffening, and as a result, it becomes possible for the tumor to retreat, condense, and fibrify[13]. Ultimately, the tumor may even completely disappear.

In a few words, this process is nothing but rapid muscle cell regenerative metabolism. Through Kiryo, I've been able to treat cancer on multiple occasions. Kiryo is capable of performing a supplementary role in concert with the three major modern medical treatments used to combat cancer—anti-cancer drugs, radiation therapy, and surgery by heightening immune function and increasing the efficacy of the above therapies.

Thus, ends my explanation of how muscular adjustment is able to bring about the effects of Kiryo. Next, I would like to explain, in simple terms, the relationship between muscular adjustment and regenerative metabolism.

(4) Muscular Adjustment Causes Regenerative Metabolism, and Becomes the Driving Force for the Normal Function of Muscle Cells

Muscular adjustment causes the regenerative metabolism of one's own skeletal muscles, viscera and visceral muscles, and it is the driving force for the wholesome, normal function of the muscle cells that comprise these tissues. In order for rapid regenerative metabolism to occur, both good blood circulation—as is caused by blood flow adjustment which ensures delivery of

---

[13] Transform into fibers.

72

oxygen and nutrients to every corner of the body—and good internal gas exchange, or internal respiration (cellular respiration)—as is caused by respiratory adjustment—are needed. As a result, waste products are carried away from and expelled outside the body and its cells.

To add onto this, blood circulation causes lymph to be circulated to every corner of the body, improving immune function (immune adjustment). Additionally, blood circulation delivers hormones to the organ that needs it (hormonal adjustment).

Even further, blood circulation increases one's heat energy, elevating one's core body temperature (body temperature adjustment). Finally, once the body is recovered and restored, and is made healthy, the spirit and psyche are stabilized (mental adjustment).

(5) Blood Flow Adjustment: Effective in the Restoration of Arteriosclerosis

Blood circulation refers to the process by which the blood passes through the heart and blood vessels to travel to every corner of the body. When blood circulation becomes poor, the resulting state is referred to as *insufficient blood flow* (circulation). Improving and fixing insufficient blood flow is referred to as *blood flow adjustment* or *blood circulation adjustment*.

Blood flow (blood circulation) adjustment is the fixing of abnormalities in blood flow or the repair of excess or insufficient blood flow. The heart and blood vessels are what carry out this blood flow adjustment. But what moves the heart and blood vessels? The answer is the autonomic nervous system. The autonomic nervous system is what repeatedly contracts and expands the heart and blood vessels, driving blood circulation.

When exchange of healing life-energy (neurotransmissive exchange) begins, what happens?

The answer is the activation of the sensory stiffening nerve. The sensory stiffening nerve works in concert (unifies) with the autonomic nervous system to control (oversee) the heart and blood vessels. The sensory

73

stiffening nerve causes sustained instantaneous stiffening in the muscles (skeletal and visceral), causing muscular adjustment, which makes all the muscles in the body softer.

In a similar fashion, the sensory stiffening nerve instructs the contractions and expansions of the heart and muscle cells to be stronger and more vigorous. It does this by coupling the instantaneous stiffening contraction of the muscles with the instantaneous contraction of the blood vessels, and the relaxation of the muscles with the expansion of the blood vessels.

We will call this instantaneous contraction and expansion of the blood vessels, caused by sustained instantaneous stiffening of the muscles *sustained instantaneous contraction*. Sustained instantaneous contraction makes the heart (cardiac muscle) itself softer, allowing its contractions and expansions to become larger and more pronounced.

Additionally, the contractions and expansions of the coronary arteries also grow larger and more pronounced, improving blood flow throughout the heart and heightening its function. Blood vessels throughout the body (arteries, veins and lymphatic vessels) respond to this change in the heart, and their contractions and expansions also grow larger. In particular, their expansions grow larger and more pliant. As a result, blood circulation throughout the body is improved. This improved blood circulation is nothing but the Kiryo concept of blood flow adjustment.

The quality of one's blood flow can be determined from one's pulse at the wrist. The pulse should be checked before doing Kiryo exercise or performing Kiryo healing.

The pulse of a healthy individual is regular and maintains a stable rate. However, for an ailing individual, the rate, intensity, and regularity of the pulse is variable. When checking the pulse after Kiryo exercise or Kiryo healing, we should see that it changes into a good, stable rhythm.

To express this change in the pulse with Kiryo terminology, we can say, as mentioned before, that the blood vessels in the wrist become wider and softer, and thus the contractions and relaxations of these vessels become larger and more pronounced. Consequently, the blood inside these vessels flows composedly, constantly, and with vigor. In Kiryo terminology, this is referred to as a *composed pulse*.

It is this composed pulse that is the proof of good blood circulation.

74

A composed pulse is the manifestation of blood flow adjustment and signifies good blood circulation. I discussed the activity of the sensory stiffening nerve using examples of the manifestation of corporal healing effects, but to explain in a few words, the sensory stiffening nerve also has a function that causes blood flow adjustment (composed pulse), or good blood flow, which carries out rapid regenerative metabolism. This is the secret of the wonderful effects of Kiryo, and the answer to the mystery with which I grappled with for so long.

Next, I would like to discuss the effects of Kiryo on the disease of arteriosclerosis. [14] Some representative examples of arteriosclerosis are cerebral and coronary arteriosclerosis. The activity of the sensory stiffening nerve brings about elasticity (wideness and softness) in the blood vessels, and so makes the flow of the blood inside these vessels composed, constant, and strong.

Because of this, cerebral arteriosclerosis is recovered and restored, and Kiryo effects can be seen when using it to treat conditions such as cerebral hemorrhage, subarachnoid hemorrhage, and cerebral infraction. In addition, Kiryo is capable of preventing the occurrence of sclerosis. In a similar fashion, coronal arteriosclerosis can be recovered and restored, and Kiryo effects can be seen in angina pectoris and cardiac infarction.

(6) Internal Respiration (Cellular Respiration) Caused by Internal Gas Exchange Manifests These Effects

I have seen individuals suffering from chronic illnesses receive Kiryo healing. Their faces, once twisted by pain, begin to regain their vitality, and they form idyllic expressions of peace. I failed to understand for a very long time why exactly Kiryo had this sort of effect on them.

As I discussed in the section on the *three healing adjustments*, the truth is that I eventually understood that these effects were due to the internal respiration (cellular respiration) caused by muscular and blood flow adjustment. I realized that this was because the internal gas exchange between oxygen and carbon dioxide was good.

---

[14] the thickening and hardening of the walls of the arteries, occurring typically in old age.

Since Kiryo involves natural breathing, which is dictated by the autonomic nervous system, there is no need to for one to consciously inhale and exhale and perform external respiration. In other words, it does not require a breathing method to take place. Kiryo only needs one to feel as they are and be as they are. It entrusts the physiological phenomena (bodily phenomena) to the functions (orders) of the brainstem. Kiryo places great importance on the process of internal respiration; indeed, it is one of its major premises. This is because if internal respiration (cellular respiration), brought about by internal gas exchange, is improved, then external respiration is also naturally improved. If Kiryo exercise and Kiryo healing are carried out, then internal and external respiration will automatically improve.

Because respiration, when affected by Kiryo, becomes composed, it is referred to in the field as composed respiration. In Kiryo, internal respiration is an easy matter.

Internal respiration is the manifestation of respiratory adjustment, and it's one of the important occurrences, alongside muscular and blood flow adjustment, that takes place as part of the three adjustments principle. According to conventional medicine, respiration at the cellular level, that is, internal respiration, plays an indispensable role in energy production.

During respiration there are three core processes. First is the intake of oxygen from the air into the lungs. The second is the bringing of blood, which has taken up the oxygen in the lungs, to every corner of the body via the heart and blood vessels. The third is carrying out, in each cell of the body, the gas exchange between oxygen brought to it by the blood and carbon dioxide.

Carbon dioxide is brought to the lungs by the veins, where it is expelled outside of the body. When considering the processes of respiration, the first to note is external respiration. The second is blood flow adjustment. The third is internal respiration (cellular respiration) which is caused by internal gas exchange.

In Kiryo, this third process is referred to as respiratory adjustment. When internal respiration (respiratory adjustment) becomes good, external respiration will also naturally become good.

(7) Immune Adjustment (Lymphatic Vessel Adjustment) Activates Immune Cells, Restoring Regenerative Metabolism

(A) Lymphatic Vessel Adjustment

White blood cells encompass a great number of different types of cells, including monocytes, granulocytes, and lymphocytes.

What sort of paths do these white blood cells pass through as they circulate around the body?

White blood cells are created in the marrow inside our bones and are sent to the tissues of our extremities via blood vessels. White blood cells contained in our bodily fluids are sucked up by the capillary blood vessels and capillary lymphatic vessels that encircle our tissues.

There are many lymph nodes contained throughout our lymphatic vessels. The sucked-up lymph passes through these lymph nodes and the thoracic duct, enters the blood vessels through a fork in the subclavian vein, and then enters the heart, and finally passes through the arteries to reach the capillary blood vessels. From these capillaries, it diffuses into our tissues, and is then again taken up by capillary lymphatic vessels before entering the lymphatic vessel system. This is the circulatory course that the lymph takes.

Now then, how exactly does the lymph inside the lymphatic vessels flow through them?

The flow of lymph follows the same fundamental principles as the flow of blood inside the veins. However, the lymph that travels through the lymphatic vessels does not flow up and down the body via the action of the heart. The lymph above the heart is pulled down by gravity, and naturally flows downward. Lymph below the heart is pumped upward by the contraction and relaxation of the muscles.

The lymphatic vessels circulate lymph by coordinating with the contractions and relaxations of the skeletal (like those of your arms and legs) and visceral muscles throughout the body. Like the heart and blood vessels, lymphatic vessels are made to function by the autonomic nervous system. Via the exchange of healing life-energy that takes place in Kiryo exercise and Kiryo healing, the autonomic nervous system and sensory stiffening nerve are unified and muscular adjustment is then carried out. At the same time, blood flow adjustment is carried out. Simultaneously, adjustment of the lymph vessels occurs.

In response to the muscular adjustment caused by sustained instantaneous stiffening, that is, instantaneous stiffening contractions and relaxations, the contractions and expansions of the lymphatic vessels become larger and more pronounced. As a result, lymph flow (circulation), linked to blood flow adjustment, is improved. This activity of the lymphatic vessels is referred to as *lymphatic vessel adjustment.*

To confirm whether or not lymphatic vessel adjustment has occurred, all that we need do is check the patient's arterial pulse at their wrist or similar area. This is because the lymph flows inside the arteries itself. If the pulse is a composed pulse, then we can be sure that the lymphatic vessels have been adjusted, and that the lymph is flowing through them well as it circulates throughout the body.

(B) Immune Cell Adjustment: Immune Cell Differentiation

The red blood cells, white blood cells, and platelets that make up our blood are born from the pluripotent stem cells inside our bone marrow. First, these cells are divided into blood-type cells and lymphocyte-type cells. After this, the blood-type cells finish their differentiation inside the marrow itself, but the lymphocyte-type cells are differentiated inside the lymph tissues.

The blood-type cells are differentiated into red blood cells, granulocytes (white blood cells), and platelets. Granulocytes are differentiated into eosinophils, neutrophils, basophils, and monoblasts. Monoblasts eventually become monocytes; which are differentiated into dendritic cells and macrophages, among others.

On the other hand, the lymphocyte-type cells made in the bone marrow enter the lymphatic system through the capillary lymphatic vessels and then proliferate and differentiate in the lymph nodes, thymus, and spleen. Eventually, these lymphocytes differentiate into all the various types of immune cells. Immune cells include B cells (humoral cell), T cells, and natural killer cells (cell-mediated immunity).

To summarize, the granulocytes of the blood and the lymphocytes of the lymph are both white blood cells. White blood cells are the primary component of the immune system. Exchange of healing life-energy (Kiryo exercise/Kiryo healing) causes not only muscular and blood flow (heart/blood vessel) adjustment, but also simultaneously causes lymphatic vessel adjustment. It is through these processes that blood and lymph circulation becomes good and proper.

When lymph flow becomes good and proper, nutrients and oxygen are provided to lymph cells, enabling them to differentiate and proliferate well. We can surmise that because of this, immune cells, like the B, T, and NK cells, are activated and their regenerative metabolism is improved.

When the immune cells are activated and being regeneratively metabolized, the immune system is strengthened, and it is able to heal injuries and illnesses. It is also able to protect against the future occurrence of illness. This is one of the healing adjustments of body and mind known in Kiryo as immune adjustment.

(C) The Primitive Brain System and the Ancient Immune System: Primeval Life Functions

Just as we were able to use Kiryo to empirically prove the existence of the primitive brainstem, we can use conventional science to prove that an ancient immune system exists. I will now introduce this ancient immune system as given by modern medical science.

o Reverse Evolution

When emergency situations arise, the human body switches over to its ancient immune system. An old mechanism used to monitor the abnormal cells in one's body also remains, and when the body falls into an emergency state, this mechanism is switched on, and reacts to the threat.

o A Primeval System Still Lives On

Lymphocytes were originally born as part of a system designed to purge abnormal cells from within the body. Only later did they evolve into a system capable of detecting and attacking foreign invaders (foreign antigens). Nevertheless, though they may have evolved, they did not simply lose their older function. Though it might have lost a small amount of the power it used to have, this old system still lives on in us today.

When the body is faced with an emergency, it reduces the power of the anti-antigen immune system, and the ancient system is revived. For example, when one is infected by a virus, or is under great stress, or is continually taking some great damage, the advanced immune system possessed and overseen by cells, such as one's T and B, etc., is weakened. Subsequently, a switch activating the system below this advanced one—one that fights against enemies of the body without the power of the antigen-antibody reaction—is flipped.

If the emergency situation continues for longer, the body switches to a system that is one additional level older. This is how the system being used to fight the emergency state the body is being placed under is gradually and incrementally downgraded until the body is eventually unable to make use of its advanced immune weaponry to combat foreign invaders. If the body reaches this state, one's life is in considerable danger.

○ The Autonomic Nervous System and Hormones Flip the Switch

The neurotransmitters noradrenaline and dopamine, secreted by the sympathetic nerves of the autonomic nervous system, and the hormones adrenaline and glucocorticoid, secreted by the adrenals, are what flip the immune switch. One of the changes that prompts flipping of this switch is aging. Once one passes the age of 20, the thymus, which creates T and B cells, begins to grow weak. In fact, this weakening is another change caused by the flipping of this switch.

Even when we are young, if, through great stress, infectious disease, cancer, or pregnancy, our energy reserves deplete, and we fall into a state of emergency, the switch is flipped.[15]

The existence of this complicated system and its wondrous capabilities never fails to amaze me. When injury or illness places the body into a state of emergency, the remnant ancient immune system incrementally activates itself. Of course, given that we have already discussed how the

---

[15] *An Illustrated Trivia: Toru Abo's 'The Organization of the Immune System that Prevents You from Getting Sick* by Toru Abo, Natsume Publishing, 2008

primitive brainstem lies dormant in our current brainstem, the presence of this ancient system should be of no great surprise. In fact, we might even be inclined to think of its existence as obvious, or predictable. It's simply that we just haven't noticed it yet.

I believe that which allows for the manifestation of the wonderful healing effects of Kiryo is the activation of the primitive brainstem and the ancient immune system. Thus, we will refer to the primitive brainstem and the ancient immune system together as "primeval life functions."

(D) Hormonal Adjustment: Homeostasis

At the beginning of my amateur era, I was asked by a woman in her 40's to take a look at her ovarian cyst, and so I performed some Kiryo healing on it. The next day, when I saw her again, she told me that she had, "woken up that morning to wash her face, and it felt so moist." Her ovaries had been restored, and the internal secretion of her female hormones had become good and proper.

Similarly, I have performed Kiryo healing on many men, all of whom declare afterwards that they feel, "so alive", and, "so energized!" This, too, is an effect of proper internal secretion of male hormones.

In the world of Kiryo, we have a saying that goes: "Women should be womanly, and men manly." In the case of women, we also say that, "their skin should be moist, they should be beautiful, and look young." This is precisely because Kiryo has effects on beauty and health.

This process is referred to as *hormonal adjustment*. But what exactly are the "hormones" that we are speaking of here?

(E) Hormones: Their Function and Role

Hormones are substances internally secreted (increted) from endocrine glands (endocrine organs) that circulate around the body with the other bodily fluids, and are responsible for bringing about specific, defined changes to specialized tissues. Hormones are synthesized in the body's various

81

endocrine glands and increted directly into the bloodstream where they then circulate throughout the body, affecting certain organs and regulating the body as a whole.

Hormones, alongside the nerves, are responsible for transmitting communicative signals between organs and maintaining bodily homeostasis. Hormones (of the endocrine type) function in intimate coordination with the autonomic nervous system. They also have the responsibility of returning the body to normal in the event of various external and internal stimuli causing changes to it. This is what is referred to as homeostasis. The brainstem performs the same homeostatic function when it tells the body to, "live on, live on."

(F) The Autonomic Nervous System, Sensory stiffening nerve, and Hormonal Adjustment

As is well-known, if the number of hormones in the body grows either too small or too great, the general condition of the body begins to suffer. The autonomic nervous system is responsible for controlling hormonal levels because it coordinates hormone incretion.

So then, how exactly does the mechanism of hormonal adjustment through the exchange of healing life-energy work?

It turns out that by the orders of the wholesome brainstem (homeostatic life maintenance), the autonomic nervous system and sensory stiffening nerve work together to effect hormonal adjustment.

To explain in more detail, we first start with sustained instantaneous stiffening, which brings about muscular adjustment. With exception to the endocrine organ located within our brain, all endocrine organs inside the body are muscle, and as such, they contract and relax to function properly. The activity of the sensory stiffening nerve brings about muscular adjustment, and the muscular tissue of each endocrine organ then begins to contract and relax in a good and proper way, thereby heightening its functional capability. Of course, the autonomic nervous system also follows suit.

Next, the autonomic nervous system instructs each endocrine organ to secrete the appropriate amount of each hormone. The autonomic nervous

82

system itself is actually stimulated to function by hormones.

Many of the women who come to the Kiryo Academy to learn, suffer from sensitivity to cold. Though, at the beginning of their training, they may be considered "cold women", they eventually become "hot women", and eventually "blazing women". I wrote about this in a bit of a joking manner, but the phenomenon itself is true and very routine.

A similar transition happened with me. Though I was physically weak, often ill, and susceptible to cold as a child, I began following Kiryo practice and, while I never quite made it to the level of "blazing", I would say that I was able to transform into a "hot man". Even now, I am a "hot man".

I, and almost all Kiryo practitioners, have had our body temperature adjusted by Kiryo. With regards to the activity pattern of the autonomic nervous system, I would say that almost all people involved with Kiryo are parasympathetic types.

Please look at the explanations I have given thus far for each of the healing adjustments of body and mind. I believe readers will be able to understand just how the placement of the parasympathetic nerves in a central (superior) role, while improving the function of the sympathetic nerves, can lead to the raising of one's core body temperature. Each of these healing adjustments of body and mind are also quite effective against cancer.

(H) Mental Adjustment: Stabilization of Spirit and Psyche

Modern-day Japan is often called a "stress society". As I have said before, what with the glut of information, messages, and things to which we are exposed, things can become quite bewildering. Time itself seems to pass with astonishing speed.

The idea that in life, one ought to, "fall seven times but get up eight", is perhaps already a relic of the past. After falling and getting up but once, we find that times have already moved on to a new age, advancing with such a speed that we cannot help but be left behind. Interpersonal relationships have become shallow, and many of us are plagued by feelings of loneliness.

Those of today's society have brainstems that, unable to keep up with the cognitive expansion of the cerebrum, are experiencing a weakening of their vital force. This vital weakening of the brainstem causes dysfunction of the autonomic nervous system. Except for a few special illnesses, almost all disease is caused by dysfunction of the autonomic nervous system. Autonomic dysfunction brings many forms of trouble to all the body's organs.

The symptoms of autonomic dysfunction can be divided into the psychological and the physiological. These symptoms are interrelated. Things like stress first appear as psychological symptoms but then begin to cause physiological problems, which then subsequently cause further psychological problems: amounting to an ever-worsening cycle of degrading health.

Worries or Symptoms Brought about by Autonomic Dysfunction

o Psychological Symptoms

These include: becoming annoyed, feeling uneasy, feeling depressed, feeling unmotivated, being unable to concentrate, being quick to anger, being easily troubled by small things, feeling sad, feeling lonely, being forgetful, becoming inattentive, and feeling apathetic—among others.

o Physiological Symptoms

These include: Tiring easily, having heart palpitations, feeling sluggishness, experiencing vertigo, lacking appetite, difficulty falling asleep, having light sleep, difficulty staying asleep, difficulty waking in the morning, persistent sleepiness, hot flashes, unsteadiness, trouble walking, a feeling of heaviness, shallow breathing, trouble breathing, heartburn, dizziness, and susceptibility to cold—among others.

People come with various complaints. In fact, you may even think of undefined or variant complaints as the hallmark of autonomic dysfunction.

Let us consider the psychological and physiological symptoms of autonomic dysfunction from the perspective of the function of the autonomic nervous system.

The sympathetic nerves help us respond in times of stress. The parasympathetic nerves help us relax. Given this, it makes sense that autonomic dysfunction arises from psychological and physiological stress.

When we are stressed, the sympathetic nerves are working quite hard. And because the purpose of the parasympathetic nerves is to help us relax, during periods of stress they are at their weakest. Which means that in times of stress, the function of the autonomic nervous system as a whole is tilted in favor of the sympathetic nervous system and is unable to return to a state where the parasympathetic nerves are also working. That is, the autonomic nervous system becomes unable to switch, or change, from relying on the sympathetic nerves to relying on the parasympathetic nerves.

So, what do we do?

We force ourselves to switch from a biased over-reliance on the sympathetic nerves to one that accommodates the parasympathetic nerves as well.

This switch is left to Kiryo. The primitive brainstem is awakened via exchange of healing life-energy, transitioning the brainstem into the wholesome brainstem (primitive brainstem and modern medical brainstem together).

The wholesome brainstem places the parasympatheticarm of the autonomic nervous system in a superior (central) role, at the same time sending commands to the sensory stiffening nerve. The parasympathetic nerves and the sensory stiffening nerve couple (unify) together and manifest corporal healing effects.

These corporal healing effects bring about comprehensive adjustments simultaneously throughout the body; including muscular adjustment, blood flow adjustment, respiratory adjustment, immune adjustment, hormonal adjustment, and body temperature adjustment. These comprehensive adjustments help bring balance back to the division of work between the sympathetic and parasympathetic nerves and return the function of the autonomic nervous system to normal.

Once the function of the autonomic nervous system is restored, the psychological and physiological symptoms of autonomic dysfunction can all be done away with at once. The uncertain, ill-defined complaints of patients disappear. As a result, mental adjustment is one of the effects of the adjustment of body and mind.

Chapter 4: Kiryo Exercise
(Mastery of the Symbiotic Healing Power): Neurotransmissive Exchange

1. The Goal of Kiryo Exercise is Mastery of the Symbiotic Healing Power

The goal of Kiryo exercise is the mastery of the ability to heal both the self and others. The average person is completely unaware of the fact that the power to heal both themselves and others exists inside themselves. And because they are unaware of its existence, they are unable to make use of this healing power. In fact, the clear majority of people pass away without ever knowing of the existence of this ability to heal the self and others.

Kiryo exercise refers to the act of using the exchange of healing life-energy to awaken the Kiryo nervous system. It may also be the act of two people mutually awakening each other's systems.

The awakening of the Kiryo nervous system is nothing but the awakening of the primitive brainstem. And the awakening of the primitive brainstem involves the awakening of the ancient immune system. This awakens the primeval life functions.

In other words, Kiryo exercise causes the awakening of the primeval life functions themselves. These primeval life functions are the root of our healing abilities. The power of Ki is nothing but the power to heal. Self-healing-power and other-healing-power together are known as the *symbiotic healing power*.

If we liken healing power to a flower, then the flower of one's natural healing power is already in bloom. Thus, we will refer to the process of awakening the symbiotic healing power that lies dormant inside us as *blossoming our symbiotic healing power*.

86

Let us together blossom the source of health itself that lies dormant within us, our symbiotic healing power.

2. Things to Keep in Mind When Doing Kiryo Exercise

Kiryo exercise is, in a way of speaking, the practical application of the Kiryo way of thought. While I have previously explained the logical considerations relevant to mastery of symbiotic healing power, I would like to mention here a few additional things to keep in mind.

(1) Let Yourself Feel as You Are

Kiryo exercise is almost all feedback-based exchange. We achieve our natural bodies by participating in this feedback exchange.

When we perform Kiryo exercise, neurotransmissive exchange either awakens our own Kiryo nervous systems (solo Kiryo exercise) or helps us and others mutually awaken each other's Kiryo nervous systems. In other words, it is the awakening of the primitive brainstem.

In order to awaken our primitive brainstems, we form the ku-no-ji form with our five fingers and palm, then we simply *feel as we are;* Doing so enables our perceptive differentiation to work. This is our one and only method. There is no need to invent additional, complicated methods of practice.

(2) Let Yourself Experience Sensory Stiffening as You Are

Kiryo exercise is the practice of just *being as you are.* When one begins feedback exchange, the moment one begins to feel the Ki energy entering their body, their ku-no-ji palm will naturally—before they themselves realize it—begin to stiffen. In some people, their entire body will experience the stiffening phenomenon, and their hands will begin to move entirely

87

independent of their own will (innate stiffening/manifest stiffening).

This phenomenon is caused by sensory stiffening brought about by order of the brainstem (sensory stiffening nerve). This sort of sensory stiffening phenomenon is what causes muscular adjustment via sustained instantaneous stiffening.

Here, the phrase "as you are" really just means, "experience sensory stiffening as you are." This "as you are" principle, a bodily manifestation of corporal healing effects, forms the core of Kiryo itself.

(3) The Palm of the Five-Fingered *Ku no ji* Palm is a Symbol of Kiryo

When beginning Kiryo healing, it is crucial that one make one's hand and palm into the five-fingered ku-no-ji form. The five-fingered ku-no-ji palm is a symbol of Kiryo itself.

During neurotransmissive exchange, the exchange of healing life-energy, the *ku no ji* palm becomes able to perceive and differ. It is in this state that one ought to continue the Kiryo practice by simply *feeling as they are.*

As this perceptive and differentiating ability heightens, before one realizes it, a feeling of stiffening will appear in the ku-no-ji palm, and its sensory stiffening ability will also heighten. The ku-no-ji palm should remain *as it is* in this stiffened state.

The converse is also true; we can say that as sensory stiffening ability becomes stronger, the perceiving and differentiating ability also grows stronger. Thus, the perceptive and differentiating ability and the sensory stiffening ability are reciprocally affected by each other and are but two sides of the same coin.

The perception/ differentiating ability and the sensory stiffness ability are but orders from the brainstem. If the perceptive differentiating ability and the sensory stiffening ability become stronger, then one becomes able to awaken one's primitive brainstem. And if one is able to awaken one's primitive brainstem, then one's primeval life functions, that is, the symbiotic healing power, is improved.

88

Initially, I think that most people will not be able to feel a sensation of feedback or achieve any sort of perceptive differentiating ability. However, I urge readers to persist. Once one develops their perceptive/differentiating ability, one's sensory stiffness ability will naturally develop as well.

It is believed that during the dawn of humanity, when we were just beginning to achieve bipedal locomotion, our hands were very similar to the five-fingered ku-no-ji palm. We were unable to move our five short fingers back then as freely and gracefully as we can move them now. For this reason, the ku-no-ji palm used in Kiryo closely resembles the hands we humans had in our primeval age. Thus, we will call the five-fingered ku-no-ji palm the *ancient palm*." The *ancient palm* is a physical, symbolic representation of the shape of Kiryo itself. This ancient palm is what awakens our primitive brainstems.

(4) There Are Two Individual Differences in the Perception and Differentiation Ability of the Palm

Kiryo exercise (neurotransmissive exchange) stimulates the perceptive differentiation ability in the ku no ji palm. And there are two individual differences in this ability.

The first is that, depending on the person, the absolute perceptive ability of their ku no ji palm may vary. The second is that there may be differences in the type of feedback sensation felt by each person in their ku no ji palm. Though we are all sensing the same life energy, the specific sensation each of us feels may be different.

For a detailed breakdown of each sensation, please take a look at Figure 3 on page 38: "Feedback Sensation Types at a Glance." Every single one of us can feel at least one of the sensations listed therein. Additionally, while we cannot feel feedback sensations as distinctly with the soles of our feet, the sensations felt there are still similar to those felt in our hands.

(5) Life-Energy is Healing Life-Energy

We, just like animals and pets, give off life-energy just by existing. Life-energy may be called Ki, or Ki energy, or healing life-energy. The truth is that, despite the fact that we give off life-energy at all times, most of us live our lives entirely unaware of this fact.

(6) Healing Life-Energy (Kiryo Life Energy) is Neurotransmissive Exchange

When the exchange of healing energy begins through the ku-no-ji palm that is *"feeling as it is,"* the Kiryo nervous system (primitive brainstem, Kiryo nerves, perceptive differentiation nerve, sensory stiffening nerve) is awakened. This is a communicative exchange between the outside of the body and the nerves caused by a mutual awakening of Kiryo nervous systems. An interaction that is neurotransmissive exchange (healing neurostimulatory exchange). Thus, healing energy exchange is also neurotransmissive exchange.

When Kiryo exercise or Kiryo healing begins, Kiryo life energy is generated inside the body (primitive brainstem). This generated Kiryo energy is emitted through the ku-no-ji palm.

Let us keep the above six points in mind when performing Kiryo exercise.

3. Neurotransmissive Exchange Occurs Even in Solo Kiryo Exercise

Kiryo exercise can be practiced even when one is alone. We, just like animals, give off life-energy, that is, healing life-energy, just by existing. One can feel the healing energy they emit with one's own ku-no-ji palm. This is exactly what solo Kiryo exercise is.

Join both hands together in front of your chest. Next, separate the palms of your hands by about 4 inches. Next, make the five fingers and palm of each hand into the ku-no-ji form. The healing life-energy is now being emitted from the ku-no-ji palms of both your right and left hands.

Initially, most people will not be able to feel a thing. However, if you

90

continue to practice Kiryo exercise, you will slowly begin to feel a slight sensation. Most people will first feel it in their left hand. Beginning to feel the sensation for the first time means that one's perceptive differentiation nerve has begun to work.

The healing life-energy coming from one's left hand and the healing life-energy coming from one's right hand are now intermingling and exchanging with one another. Eventually, the healing energy being exchanged in both the right and left ku-no-ji palms will begin to be felt as a feedback sensation. Subsequently, in both the right and left ku-no-ji palms, one will begin to feel a slight stiffening feeling.

Beginning to feel this slight stiffening means that one's sensory stiffening nerve has begun to work. That is, one has developed the perceptive differentiation ability as well as the sensory stiffening ability.

Put another way, healing life-energy is being emitted from both the left and the right ku-no-ji palm, and the perceptive differentiation nerve is perceiving and differentiating this healing energy in each hand. This means that one is perceiving the healing life-energy that is entering from outside the body. This is simply neurotransmissive exchange outside of the body. Thus, even in solo Kiryo healing, neurotransmissive exchange is occurring.

The strong orders then given by the wholesome brainstem cause the *three adjustments principle* to be manifested as corporal healing effects, as well as causing the healing adjustment of body and mind. The healing adjustment of body and mind causes the awakening and manifestation of the primeval life functions, which are the root of symbiotic healing power. The manifestation of the primeval healing functions heightens one's symbiotic healing power and leads to the mastery of it.

In the case of my father, he enjoyed practicing Kiryo exercise alone. He would often separate his hands by the requisite amount and perform the energy exchange on his own.

One day, a neighbor was over at his house for some tea and light conversation when she began to have a headache. My father, more as a test than anything, did some healing on her, and her pain subsided quite quickly. News of this spread in the neighborhood, and my father ended up having to perform Kiryo healing on many people.

Such news tends to dramatically spread, and eventually my father ended up in the local newspaper. At that time, he was 75 years old. Until he

91

died at the age of 87, he continued to perform Kiryo healing on those around him and was thanked by many for his services.

My father used to often say that he was "the happiest person in the world to have received this gift." He made use of his symbiotic healing power to help many people.

(1) Kiryo Exercise Between Palms Improves Symbiotic Healing Power

Let us now take a look at the function of the fingers on our hands. It is believed that when humans first began to walk on two legs, the function of the fingers of our hands was sensory activity, as part of a sensory network centered around the primitive brainstem.

The *sensory activity* we speak of here is the use of one's hands and feet, and whole body to sense the invisible life-energy emitted by plants and animals; we call this sensory activity "healing sensation." At this time in our history, our cerebrum was still underdeveloped, and we therefore lived relying only on sensory activity that was centered around the primitive brainstem.

Eventually, the five fingers on each of our hands learned to hold things and to use tools, and we thus developed an enhanced ability to learn. This learning ability spurred the development of the cerebrum and led to the heightening of our motor function enough that we were able to move our five fingers individually. It is thought that a high degree of motor coordination was needed for us to grasp things or to use tools more effectively, and so our five fingers evolved to meet our needs. In response to, and alongside, this process, our cerebrum began to develop and evolve as well.

The developed cerebrum we possess today affords us a robust capacity to think and advanced intellectual capacity (intellectual function). It is thought that, in the years to come, the cognitive capabilities of the cerebrum will continue to expand.

Our advanced cognitive abilities allow us to move, at our own will, the five fingers on each of our hands freely in difficult and precise ways. Our five fingers spurred the development of our cerebrum, and now it is our

92

cerebrum (and its orders) that guides our fingers as we wish. Yet, we also must remember that our cerebrum suppresses the healing sensory activity of our brainstem.

The five fingers of our hands are fulfilling the motor functions dictated to them by our cognitive activity. And most people believe that this motor function is the sole purpose of our fingers. Have we completely lost the brainstem-mediated "healing sensory function" of our fingers?

No! The truth is that this ability lies latent within our bodies. It is just that the only proof we have of this brainstem-ordered healing sensory activity is the small amount of sensory ability manifest in the palms of our hands and the soles of our feet. In particular, we still can still faintly sense healing sensations in our five fingers.

This healing sensory ability of our five fingers is, as I have explained before, the specific, practical entrance by which we can once again move from the world of cognitive thought to the world of sensation. This means that, in the present day, the five fingers on our hands have two functions: a cognitively-mediated motor function and a sensory-mediated healing sensory function, the latter of which is dormant. I would like to examine these two functions.

(2) The Fingers on our Hands Have Two Functions

1. Our Fingers as Cognitively-Mediated Motor Units Ordered by the Cerebrum

The five fingers on each of our hands perform motor functions; we move them without much thought and in whatever way we choose to. The five fingers on each of our hands can touch objects, grasp them, pick them up, and dangle them; they are capable of delicate and complicated movements.

With that said, let us now examine the functions of our fingers from the perspective of nervous function.

Moving our fingers according to our own will is done through orders issued by the cerebrum and is therefore a cerebral function. The nerves that are responsible for actually moving our fingers once they have received orders from the cerebrum are the motor nerves. And the reason we can feel things when we touch them is because we have sensory nerves. Simply put, the five fingers on each of our hands are motor-nerve-fingers controlled by the nervous system known to conventional medicine: the cerebrum, the motor nervous system, and the sensory nervous system.

2. Our Fingers as Sensory Activity-Mediated Healing Sensory Units Ordered by the Cerebellum

We emit life-energy just by existing. Of course, this healing life-energy is being emitted from the five fingers on each of our hands. Kiryo is nothing but the act of heightening this healing life-energy through Kiryo exercise.

The five fingers on each of our hands have the ability to perceive and differentiate the life-energy of animals and plants, as well as the ability to effect sensory stiffening—that is, the ability to cause (sustained) instantaneous stiffening contractions—in response to a life-energy stimulus lies latent.

Now, then, what must we do to heighten this healing sensory function (healing sensory activity), that is, the perceptive differentiative ability and the sensory stiffening ability?

The answer is to form the ku-no-ji palm: the symbol of Kiryo itself (the ancient palm). The ku-no-ji palm has the very important role of tying together Kiryo theory and Kiryo practice.

Why exactly do we make the ku-no-ji palm? The answer is that by putting our fingers together to make the five-fingered ku-no-ji palm, our five fingers become as one, and so perception differentiating ability and sensory stiffening ability function more effectively across the entire ku-no-ji palm.

When exchanging with a strong life energy, the perception/differentiation ability and sensory stiffening ability of our healing sensory functions also becomes stronger in a directly proportional manner. During Kiryo, one should not move one's fingers willfully; this is because doing so will activate one's motor nerves.

However, there are times when the fingers of the five-fingered ku-no-ji palm will be moved by sensory stiffening. In these situations, healing sensory function actually becomes stronger. For example, regarding the scene of me exchanging energy with a rhinoceros in Kenya, which was broadcasted

94

on Asahi TV, the rhino's energy was so strong that the moment I began the exchange with my ku-no-ji palm, my hand clenched into a fist.

Healing sensory function lies latent throughout our entire body, all the way to our fingertips: it exists only very faintly. The Kiryo nervous system (primitive brainstem, Kiryo nerves, perceptive differentiation nerve, and sensory stiffening nerve) is its foundation.

Figure 8: The Ku no Ji Palm: The Protocol (Feedback Sensation)

Cognitive side	(1)	Relax the palm of your hand, and ready it in the proper position.
Cognitive side	(2)	Arrange your five fingers and palm into the *ku no ji* shape.
Cognitive side	(3)	In the *ku no ji* shape, allow a small amount of strength to return to your five fingers. [Lessening the suppressive activity of the cerebrum] (The desire to attempt to feel)
Natural switch	(4)	The Kiryo nerves activate (awaken) [Feeling as you are]
Perceptive Differentiation Nerve	(5)	The energy response sense begins to function.
Perceptive Differentiation Nerve	(6)	Begin feeling the sensation of healing energy exchange. (Heat, numbness, compression, cold, prickliness, tingling, itchiness, etc.)
Perceptive Differentiation Nerve	(7)	A feeling of stiffness arises in the entire *ku no ji* palm, including the five fingers.
Sensory Stiffening Nerve	(8)	Sensory stiffening begins in the *ku no ji* palm. • The *ku no ji* palm undergoes sensory stiffness as it is. • The *ku no ji* palm undergoes sensory stiffness in the shape of a clenched fist. • The fingers of the *ku no ji* palm each undergo sensory stiffness in some modified position.
Sensory Stiffening Nerve	(9)	One gains the ability to differentiate the presence of various life energy-mediated changes in the *ku no ji* palm.

Sensory side comprises the *Sensory Stiffening Nerve* and the *Perceptive Differentiation Nerve*.

Sensory Stiffening Nerve — **Be as you are**

Perceptive Differentiation Nerve — **Feel as you are**

Cognitive side — **Conscious action**

Perception / differentiation

Kiryo is unification with natural energy

Please look at Figure 8 on page 96: "Ku-no-ji Palm: The Protocol (Feedback Sensation)". Items 1, 2, and 3 under the "Cognitive Side" are mediated by cerebral orders. Natural conversion (consciousness) jumpstarts the healing Kiryo nerves, which in turn awakens the primitive brainstem.

This awakened primitive brainstem sends orders to the entire body causing the perception differentiation nerve to begin working as is delineated in items 4, 5, 6, and 7. At the same time, the sensory stiffening nerve begins functioning as is delineated in item 8. As a result of the activity of the sensory stiffening nerve, the ku-no-ji palm undergoes sensory stiffness in three configurations.

The first configuration is merely that of the usual ku-no-ji palm. Most people fall under this configuration. The second configuration is when the ku-no-ji palm takes the shape of a clenched fist. This occurs when the healing energy exchange is particularly strong. The third is when each finger independently undergoes sensory stiffness. Very few people undergo sensory stiffening in this configuration.

We can consider steps four through eight as proof of the fact that Kiryo is nothing but unification with natural energy itself. Steps four through seven, which are controlled by the perceptive differentiation nerve, are to be done while one is *feeling as they are*, while step eight, controlled by the sensory stiffening nerve, should occur when one is *being as they are*. Throughout all of this, we are relinquishing control of our five fingers to our brainstem.

Finally, in step nine, the ku-no-ji palm becomes capable of differentiating changes in the life-energy of animals, humans, and plants. In other words, one becomes capable of dividing their perceptive/differentiative ability into perception and differentiation.

When we begin to perceive energy, in response to this energy stimulus, sensory stiffening ability is activated within us. This sensory stiffening ability becomes the source of our differentiative ability. In turn, this differentiative ability strengthens our perceptive ability. This is what the term perceptive/differentiative ability" refers to.

Healing sensory function (healing sensory activity) first begins to work when we gather together our five fingers, form the ku-no-ji palm, and, without moving, *feel as we are* and *be as we are*. The healing sensory function (healing sensory activity) that occurs in our ku-no-ji palm by way of the five fingers on each of our hands extends to, via the orders of the brainstem, structures like our skeletal and visceral muscles. Thus, feedback sensation felt by the hands is also felt by the body: a whole-body feedback sensation. The mastery of the palm's symbiotic healing power that is the object of Kiryo exercise is nothing but mastery over the whole body.

4. Kiryo Exercise: Mastery of the Symbiotic Healing Power

Exercise 1: Palm Gap Exchange

Palm Gap Exchange is the most fundamental, prototypical form of Kiryo exercise.

First, we relax our mind and body. Then, we create the ku-no-ji form with our left and right hands, and space them about 4 inches apart. This is the beginning of the Kiryo neurostimulatory exchange between the Kiryo nerves (perceptive differentiation nerve, sensory stiffening nerve) of the left hand and the healing energy of the right hand; that is, it is the beginning of neurotransmissive exchange. In other words, it is the beginning of nervous adjustment.

You may not be able to feel anything at first, however, there is no need to attempt to move your body or concentrate your awareness on something. Do not think, "Come on already, Ki energy!" Just allow your ku-no-ji palms to feel as they are. Even if you cannot feel anything, neurotransmissive exchange brought about by healing energy naturally begins the moment one starts performing Kiryo exercise.

Maintain a
4-inch gap

Illustration 1: Palm Gap Exchange

Because there will not be any feedback sensation at first, we do not know what that sensation should feel like when it does occur. But the moment we feel even a faint heat or tingling, we have felt the feedback sensation and the first step is complete. All that is left is to continue practicing Kiryo exercise each day. Eventually, we will be able to manifest more apparent forms of feedback sensation (refer to Illustration 1).

*From here on out, in all my descriptions of the various forms of Kiryo exercise, I will refer to the ku-no-ji palm merely as the *palm*.

The objective of Kiryo exercise is to heighten the capabilities of, and ultimately master, the perceptive/differentiative ability and sensory stiffening ability (sustained instantaneous stiffening) in our life-energy sensing palms.

Perceptive/differentiative ability and sensory stiffening ability is communicated throughout the entire body via the perceptive differentiation and sensory stiffening nerves. Because of this, the three adjustments principle begins to manifest corporal healing effects. As a result, healing adjustment of mind and body takes place.

The three adjustments principle awakens the essential aspect of the

99

primitive brainstem: the primeval life functions. The primitive brainstem unifies with the modern brainstem to create the wholesome brainstem. Because of this, the primeval life-functions unify with our modern life-functions. Thus, the wholesome brainstem heightens our modern life-functions, carries out healing adjustment of mind and body, and brings about an overall health improvement. Alongside all of this, the symbiotic healing power is strengthened (mastered).

In Kiryo, the primitive brainstem and primeval life functions are thought to be the source of symbiotic healing power. While Palm Gap Exchange is the prototypical, fundamental form of all types of Kiryo exercise, its effects are still felt throughout the entire body. In other words, it is no exaggeration to say that mastery of the palms is tantamount to mastery of the entire body.

From the perspective of nervous function, palm gap exchange is a neurostimulatory exchange exercise that involves emitting healing life-energy from both the right and left palm, as well as sensing this emitted energy: an invisible neurotransmissive exchange. Neurotransmissive exchange is the task of awakening the Kiryo nerves (perceptive differentiation and sensory stiffening nerves) of both sides of the body. As a result, the Kiryo nerves throughout the body are awakened via the brainstem.

Let us master our symbiotic healing power by *feeling as we are* in our palms and awakening our primitive brainstems.

100

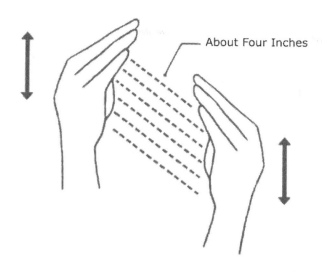

About Four Inches

Illustration 2: Palm Ki Kneading Exchange

Exercise 2: Palm Ki Kneading Exchange

Let us move our palms from their orientation in Palm Gap Exchange (Exercise 1) up and down slightly. When moving them, we should try to feel healing energy as we are doing so. Do not move your fingers, keep them in the ku-no-ji form.

Finally, let us be sure to not move both palms in the same direction. Move one palm upward, and the other down. By doing this, more life-energy is drawn out, and its flow becomes stronger. The feedback sensation triggered by neurotransmissive exchange will also become stronger.

By moving our palms (Ki kneading), the life-energy will stimulate the nerves in our palms and our perception differentiation ability and sensory stiffening ability will become stronger. Additionally, when Ki kneading, you may move both hands alternatively, independent of each other (refer to Illustration 2).

101

Illustration 3: Palm-Fingers Exchange

Exercise 3: Palm-Fingers Exchange

From the palm gap exchange (Exercise 1) orientation, slowly point the five fingers on your left hand, as if you are raising them, towards the palm of your right hand, all the while allowing them to feel as they are—refer to Illustration three.

By doing this, we will be able to feel the healing life-energy traveling down the fingers of the left hand as it enters the right palm. Once you are able to feel this, try switching the orientations of your left and right hands and continuing the exercise in this new configuration.

The nerves in our palms will be stimulated by the healing energy being sent into them. This stimulation will improve our perceptive/differentiative ability and our sensory stiffening ability. By continuing to practice Kiryo exercise every day, eventually, the feedback sensation will become quite strong. Whichever palm the feedback sensation has become stronger in, that hand will then determine your "handedness" for perception/differentiation and sensory stiffening.

Energy handedness varies from person to person, but, speaking generally, about 70% of people are left-dominant, and about 30% are right-dominant. When healing another with Kiryo healing, one should use only their dominant hand; that is, they are encouraged to use that single hand alone.

Exercise 4: Palm Opening and Closing Exchange

From the palm gap exchange (Exercise 1) configuration, we will successively broaden and narrow the gap between our palms. In this configuration, when we are opening up our palms, we will become able to notice a feeling of pulling (feeling of being tied together) in both the right and left palm (refer to Illustration 4).

Illustration 4: Palm Opening and Closing Exchange

Initially, start with about a 4-inch gap, and slowly, while feeling the healing life-energy, broaden the gap between your right and left palms. Eventually, you will be able to feel the neurotransmissive exchange sensation.

103

Once you have broadened the gap to about shoulder width, try moving your right and left palms alternatively up and down (Ki kneading). The feedback sensation should then get even stronger.

Continuing in this manner, broaden the gap between your palms as much as you can. Once you have broadened them enough, you should begin closing the gap between them. This time, the healing energy will cause a pressing feeling (compression feeling) in your palms. Further, when doing this opening and closing exercise, you will feel a variety of feedback sensations. But regardless, continue performing the opening and closing exercises.

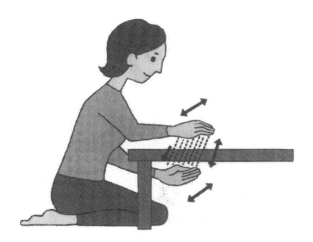

Illustration 5: Palm Trans-Desk Exchange

This exercise has the same significance as Exercises 2 and 3.

Exercise 5: Palm Trans-Desk Exchange

Once we become able to notice the life-energy exchange happening in your right and left palms, turn the hands so that your palms are facing up and down. Then, position them in relation to a desk so that the flat part of the desk lies between your palms, dividing them. Then separate your palms so there is about four inches of gap between each of them and the desk. First keep our palms in a stationary position to check that we can feel the exchange sensation (refer to Illustration 5).

Next, freely mix together the various exercise configurations we have learned so far: Palm Ki Kneading Exchange, Palm-Finger Exchange, and Palm Opening and Closing Exchange. Move your hands freely about. You should be able to sense in either hand the movement of the other, despite the fact that there is a desk between them.

The previous exercise conceals within itself a very important truth: the healing energy being emitted by both the right and left palms is capable of passing through the desk (board) without affecting whether or not it can be felt by the other hand. Our palms are capable of feeling the healing life-energy of the other via the neurostimulation it causes in the corresponding hand.

Consequently, when it comes to the symbiotic healing power, we can send healing life energy through our skeletal muscles (pectorals and abs) and reach the organs beneath to perform healing life-energy-mediated neurostimulatory exchange with them. For example, if the person receiving Kiryo healing has stomach cancer, it is possible to engage in energy exchange with the cancer-affected part of their body and heal it.

Exercise 6: Palm-Foot Exchange

The sole of our foot (scientifically, known as the plantar surface) also possesses, just like our palms, a slight healing sensory ability. Though the amount of healing life-energy emitted from the sole of the foot is in fact several times greater than that emitted from the palm.

The reason for this is that the soles of our feet, because of our bipedal nature, are always supporting the weight of our entire body, and so their sensitive function has weakened. Additionally, it is thought they became unable to feel for physiological reasons as well.

If one thinks about it, it is quite possible that no one in the history of the human race has realized that the soles of our feet have healing sensory ability. I myself was quite surprised when I realized and learned just how the sole of the human foot possesses healing sensory ability.

I first learned of the fact that the soles of both of our feet have healing sensory ability during my amateur era, while performing Kiryo healing on others. I was using my right ku-no-ji palm and placing it, in order, on the patient's head, heart, and lower abdomen to perform the healing. Additionally, as the patient was lying down, with their face up, I was performing healing energy exchange with their feet and my own palms.

Suddenly, I had a thought. I realized that because humans were initially quadrupedal, the palms of the hands and the soles of the feet were originally one and the same. I placed the sole of my right foot approximately four inches away from the soles of both of my patient's feet while I was sitting cross-legged. At first, I didn't feel anything, but after two to three minutes had passed, I was able to feel a faint twitching sensation in my foot.

I thought, "Wow! So, you can even feel it with the soles of your feet!". I continued sitting in the same posture, and the twitching sensation grew stronger. This incident was the birth of Foot-Foot Kiryo Other-*Healing*.

I realized, at that time, that the healing life-energy of the soles of the feet is more capable than what occurs in the palms, and so it is better able to help manifest Kiryo effects. Since then, the sole of the foot has become an indispensable part of Kiryo healing.

For this exercise configuration, lie on your back. Extend your right leg outward so it is straight and place your bent left leg on top of it. In this manner, we are able to place our right palm near the sole of our left foot and maintain the proper gap between the two. In this posture, we *feel as we are*, and allow the healing life-energy exchange to begin [refer to Illustration 6].

Illustration 6: Palm-Foot Exchange

Once you begin to feel the healing life-energy exchange occurring while in a stationary position, you ought to move on to alternatively moving the hand and foot. Doing so will allow a greater feeling of exchange to be felt.

The next time you do this exercise, you should exchange the orientation of your legs. It might seem ludicrous to think that the soles of our feet have any sensory capability at all, but because the healing life-energy flowing through them is quite strong, they will elicit a strong sensation in one's palms. Continue practicing the exercise, making sure to do all of the above.

Incidentally, it is okay to do this exercise while sitting in a cross-legged position or even in a chair.

Illustration 7: Foot Gap Exchange

Very few people know that healing sensory ability resides in the soles of our feet. I often call attention to this fact in a joking way. We often say that we're on our "last legs", but Kiryo makes a point of using these very legs (and the soles of the feet attached to them) in its practice, giving us a leg up on everyone else.

However, I believe that it is now high time that we realized and recognized that healing life-energy is being emitted from the soles of our feet. The foot feedback sensation felt by the soles of our feet may be dull, but they emit very strong healing life-energy. In order to ensure that this healing life-energy is awakened by our Kiryo nervous systems and in turn awakens our primitive brainstems, it becomes necessary to use the healing sensory function of the soles of our feet.

By using the soles of our feet, the three adjustments principle is manifested as a corporal healing effect, and the healing adjustment of mind and body is carried out, which brings about improvement of health. Finally, improvement and mastery of the symbiotic healing power is achieved.

Exercise 7: Foot Gap Exchange

Lie on your back, face up, and orient the soles of your feet so they are facing each other. Place them so that there is about a four-inch gap between them. Then, without moving them, allow yourself to *feel as you are* and begin the healing life-energy exchange (neurotransmissive exchange). Thus, we will be able to feel, in the stationary position, the foot feedback sensation (refer to Illustration 7). Even without any foot feedback sensation, the healing life-energy exchange is taking place.

Next, you should try freely moving your right and left soles. If you consistently practice this daily, the foot feedback sensation will slowly grow stronger. This can also be done in a cross-legged position or while sitting in a chair.

The fact that the foot feedback sensation is particularly dull, despite the strength of the healing life-energy emitted by the soles of the feet, is a unique characteristic of the sensation itself. When performing Kiryo partner-healing, this foot feedback sensation, though faint, is transmitted by the Kiryo nervous system throughout the patient's body alongside the healing life-energy being sent into the sole of the foot.

Thus, the three adjustments principle comes into play in the patient's body, and his or her body and mind are able to relax. In other words, the healing adjustment of mind and body is carried out. Because of this, the wonderful effects of Kiryo are made apparent. Spectacular healing sensory ability lies dormant in the soles of our feet. Let us be sure to make full use of it and get ourselves back on our feet.

5. Two-Person Kiryo Exercise

Two-person Kiryo exercise refers to the act of carrying out the mutual exchange of healing life-energy between oneself and another. This exchange draws out and heightens the healing life-energy of the other, and in doing so, imparts mutual healing. Furthermore, the exchanged life-energy also stimulates the nerves in the palm and causes mutual energy perception/differentiation.

When examining this process from the perspective of nervous function, it turns out that the two people participating in the exercise, by way of healing life-energy, awaken each other's Kiryo nervous systems and carry out neurotransmission—that is, neurotransmissive exchange.

Put simply, two-person Kiryo exercise is nervous healing exchange (neurostimulatory exchange) between two people. Furthermore, it ends up causing good and proper nervous adjustment throughout the bodies of both participants.

(1) Two-Person Kiryo Exercise: Palm-Palm Exchange & Sole-Sole Exchange

Palm-Palm Exchange

Palm-Palm Exchange is the most fundamental practice for achieving mastery of the symbiotic healing power.

Put together your five fingers and form them and your palm into the ku-no-ji form, taking care to not voluntarily move your fingers at all; moving them will activate your motor functions, and will halve your healing sensory function. Perform Kiryo exercise and switch the roles of who sends and who receives energy at some point midway through the practice.

Once beginning Kiryo exercise, take care to keep your five-fingered ku-no-ji palm consistent till the exercise is finished. Additionally, make sure to feel the healing life-energy *as you are*, and be in the energy flow *as you are*. At this point, the cognitive and sensory sides of the process part ways, and thus it is the point where improvement and mastery of the symbiotic healing power begins.

When healing life-energy exchange begins in the palm, almost instantaneously, a healing Kiryo space (symbiotic healing space) is formed. And when mutual healing life-energy exchange begins, the nerves of both participants are stimulated by the healing life-energy of their partner. This stimulation is sent to the brainstem, which quickly transmits it throughout the body (skeletal and visceral muscles) via the Kiryo nervous system.

Palm-Palm Exchange

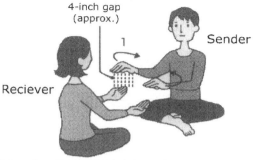

4-inch gap
(approx.)

Sender

Reciever

The receiver should point their ku no ji pam upward. The sender should place their ku no ji palm approximately four inches above their partner's hand and point it down. Next, they should make kneading motions in a clockwise or counter clockwise direction while maintaining this height.

Sender

Reciever

The sender should raise and lower their hand, thereby kneading the Ki energy between their own and their partner's palms.

Sender

Reciever

The sender should keep their hands raised high and then knead while remaining in that position.

111

By doing so, the three adjustments principle will activate, and the healing adjustment of mind and body will be simultaneously carried out. The effects of Kiryo will also begin to act against injury and illness. As we increase the number of times we practice the exercise, we will improve our symbiotic-healing power and eventually become able to master it. And because the Kiryo space between our hands is one that is used to achieve improvement and eventual mastery of the symbiotic-healing power, we will hereafter refer to it as the symbiotic-healing space.

Mastering the use of our palms is intimately connected to mastering the use of our bodies. And mastering the use of one's whole body is achieved by mastering the symbiotic-healing power itself; this is what brings about improvements in health.

Sole-Sole Exchange

It is thought that the reason we can only very faintly feel healing life energy is that the healing sensory activity of the brainstem came to be suppressed by the evolution and development of the cerebrum.

In other words, because an over-sensitive sensory faculty would actually pose a problem, the healing sensory activity of the brainstem was adjusted so that it would not hinder the cognitive faculties of the cerebrum.

When healing life-energy exchange begins in the sole of the foot, almost instantaneously, a healing Kiryo space (symbiotic healing space) is formed. The soles of our feet are exactly opposite to our hands in that their healing life-energy is several times stronger, but their feeling ability (perceptive differentiation ability) is very slight.

When mutual healing life-energy exchange begins, the nerves of both participants are stimulated by the healing life-energy of their partner. This stimulation is sent to the brainstem, which quickly transmits it throughout the body (skeletal and visceral muscles) via the Kiryo nervous system and the conventional nervous system. By doing so, the three adjustments principle will activate, and the healing adjustment of mind and body will be simultaneously carried out.

As we continue to practice the exercise, we improve our symbiotic-healing power and eventually become able to master it. In other words,

112

mastery of the symbiotic healing power achieved through the soles of the feet is just like mastery achieved through the palms of the hands. These achievements lead to symbiotic-healing power mastered throughout the whole body, which is linked to health improvement.

*Here I would like to insert something of an apology to the reader: while there are many more two-person Kiryo exercise patterns beyond those listed here, in an effort to keep the number of pages in this book down and to maintain a somewhat balanced coverage of many different topics, I have left these other exercise patterns out. I invite those interested in those additional patterns to further explore Kiryo, and if possible, visit one of the Kiryo Academies.

Sole-Sole Exchange

4-inch gap
(approx.)

Sit so there is approximately a four inch gap between
your feet. Remain in this position for some time, feeling
the healing life-energy exchange flowing through this space.

The sender should move the sole of their foot in the directions
indicated by the arrow in the diagram. The receiver should now
be able to more strongly feel the healing life-energy exchange
flowing through this space.

The sender should move the sole of their foot in the
directions indicated by the arrow in the diagram.
The receiver will feel the healing life-energy flowing
through the gap between the participants' feet.

6. Large Group Kiryo Exercise (Symbiotic Healing Power Mastery)

Large Group Kiryo exercise refers to the act of collaboratively exchanging healing life-energy among three or more people. Each person uses healing life-energy to draw out and heighten the healing life-energy of the other participants, and together they mutually heal each other. This process also involves using healing life-energy to stimulate each other's palms and soles, thereby stimulating the nerves throughout the body, which enables mutual invocation of perceptive and differentiative ability. This ultimately leads to mutual healing. Large group Kiryo exercises can be performed with anywhere from a few people to a few hundred people. Those participating in the exercise, by way of healing life-energy, awaken each other's Kiryo nervous systems and carry out neuro-transmission between all participants (neuro-transmissive exchange).

Put simply, large group Kiryo exercise is nervous healing exchange between multiple people: a process of neurostimulatory exchange. Furthermore, the exercise results in positive nervous adjustment throughout the bodies of all participants.

When Kiryo exercise brings about the beginning of healing life-energy exchange, almost instantaneously, a healing Kiryo space (symbiotic healing space) is formed between all participants. The Kiryo life-energy of each participant collects in this healing Kiryo space, giving rise to synergistic effects that allow for the creation of a robust collective life-energy. In other words, the healing Kiryo space itself becomes far stronger.

Inside the healing Kiryo space (symbiotic healing space) created during large group Kiryo exercise, the healing life-energy exchange performed by all participants in the exercise stimulates the nerves of all participants. This stimulation is sent to the brainstem, which quickly transmits stimulation throughout the body (skeletal and visceral muscles) via the Kiryo nervous system. By doing so, the three adjustments principle will activate, and the healing adjustment of mind and body will be simultaneously carried out. The effects of Kiryo will also begin to act against injury and illness. At the same time, a healing Kiryo space filled with multi-person collective life-energy enables even greater levels of improvement of the symbiotic life-force, and again enables us to quickly master the symbiotic life-force.

Here I would like to once again insert something of an apology to the reader. In an effort to keep the number of pages in this book down, and to maintain a somewhat balanced coverage of many different topics, I have had to omit images and specific explanations for many of the different configurations possible in multi-person Kiryo exercises. As such, I invite those interested in attempting such patterns to visit us at the Kiryo Academy.

To elaborate on this, I will list out the names of many different configurations of multi-person Kiryo exercise:

Brainstem Awakening Exchange; Kiryo Space Realization Exchange; Cosmic Exchange; Arrow Pinwheel Exchange; Heaven-Earth Unification Exchange; Paper Fan Exchange; Gap Transmission Exchange; Ki-Casting Exchange; Hand-Stacking Exchange; Interval Time-Keeping Exchange; Torus Exchange; Push-Out Exchange ; Columnar Exchange; Lone Sleeper Concatenated Seating Exchange; Finger-Pin Exchange; Building Exchange; Single Character Exchange; Ten Character Exchange; Sunflower Exchange; Human Dry Battery Exchange, and others.

Above, I have enumerated many different configurations of multi-person Kiryo exercise, but the main point that I would like to make is that multi-person Kiryo exercise allows for the creation of a strong collective life energy (Kiryo healing space), and thereby prompts the improvement and quick mastery of the symbiotic healing power.

7. Kiryo Self-Healing (Recovery and Restoration of Illness and Injury)

Self-healing refers to the focused use of the self-healing force to allow one to heal their own illnesses and injuries. Although people who do not have the qualifications of a physician can of course not perform medical procedures, please keep in mind that what we are referring to here is the process of using the self-healing force to treat oneself through Kiryo self-healing.

Self-healing is not a phenomenon that is well-known to the general public. In fact, the concept of self-healing itself might be completely unknown to the average person. Under Kiryo theory, while it depends somewhat on their severity, it is certainly possible to help yourself restore and recover from your illnesses and injuries.

Because Kiryo functions as a complementary, alternative treatment to conventional medical care, feel free to use Kiryo in a variety of capacities, though seeking the diagnostic advice of a medical professional is always advised.

Performing self-healing while also receiving the treatment of a medical agency will assist greatly in the recovery and restoration of your illness or injury. As for a more detailed explanation of self-healing, I will be elaborating on this subject with regards to three distinct divisions of the body: the head (brain), the torso (and its viscera), and the abdomen (and its viscera). Know that the processes in other parts of the body follow the guidelines given for the above three body parts.

(1) Kiryo Self-Healing: Head (Brain) (5-10 Minutes)

First, lie on your back [Note: This exercise can be done while sitting or standing up, but laying down improves blood flow to the brain]. Check your pulse at your wrist before beginning the exercise.

Next, select either your left or right hand, shape it into the ku-no-ji form, and place it approximately 4 inches away from the top of your head. Do not move it. By doing this, healing life-energy exchange will be able to take place between your ku-no-ji palm and head (refer to the illustration on the next page).

By doing this, you will eventually be able to faintly feel the exchange of healing life-energy between your palm and the top of your head. Once you feel it, allow yourself to simply continue feeling it *as you are*. Whether or not you feel it, the healing life-energy exchange is being carried out.

The next step is to move your hand from left to right, and up and down, in a waving motion, all the while making sure to *feel as you are*. Doing this will transmit the stimulation of the healing life-energy being exchanged which will pass through your brain and be transmitted to your body's nervous systems (Kiryo nervous system and the modern medical nervous system).

After completing all of the above, check your pulse once again. You should notice that it has changed to a composed pulse. Once healing life-energy exchange occurs between your palm and brain (cerebrum, brainstem,

117

and cerebellum), the contractions and widenings of your blood vessels will grow larger, and your blood flow will be improved. As a result, the supply of nutrients and oxygen to your brain cells will increase, and their regenerative metabolism will improve.

Head (Brain) Kiryo Self-Healing

Next, commands will be transmitted from your brainstem to the rest of your body, and the three adjustments principle will activate. As a result, the healing adjustment of the mind and body will be carried out. As far as the effects of Kiryo healing on specific illnesses are concerned, there has been demonstrated healing effects against depression and stroke (cerebral hemorrhage, cerebral infarct[16], subarachnoid hemorrhage). As well, Kiryo helps prevent these conditions from ever occurring in the first place.

(2) Kiryo Self-Healing: Torso (Organs) (10 – 15 Minutes)

---

[16] This is a common medical term used to refer to a specific type of stroke.

Note: *This exercise can be done while sitting or standing, but laying down allows your organs to more easily relax. Also, check your pulse at your wrist before beginning this exercise.*

First, lie on your back. Then select either your left or right hand, shape it into the ku-no-ji form, and place it approximately four inches away from your torso. Do not move it.

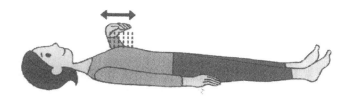

By doing this, healing life energy and affected part energy will be exchanged (neurostimulatory exchange) between your palm and the affected parts of your organs (and their muscles). Please refer to the illustration.

The next step is to move your hand from left to right, and up and down in a waving motion, all the while making sure to feel as you are. You can also move your hand in a circular motion. However, by moving your hand in a waving motion, your nerves will be better stimulated, the three adjustments principle will more easily be activated, and the healing effects of Kiryo will manifest to a greater degree.

After completing all of the above, check your pulse once again. You should notice that it has changed to a composed pulse.

Corporal Healing Effects: Three Adjustments Principle and Healing Adjustment of Mind and Body

If the organs of your torso are ailing in any way, healing life-energy exchange will be created between those ailing parts and the palm of your hand. Though

119

you may not be able to see it, healing life-energy-mediated neurostimulatory exchange is still taking place.

For another example, let's say that we have bronchitis. In that situation, the healing life-energy is being exchanged between the palm of our hand and our bronchial tubes. Once our bronchial tubes receive stimulation from the healing energy, the three healing-adjustments principle begins to take effect. As muscular adjustment begins to happen in our bronchial tubes, the blood flow inside them improves, and the muscle cells of the tubes are able to better carry out cellular respiration.

Once regenerative metabolism can take place in these cells, the muscles of the bronchial tubes become soft and supple, the airways become able to expand properly once again, and bodily respiration returns to being effortless.

The healing life-energy exchange between your palm and the affected parts of the organs elicits reactions in tissues throughout your body and leads to the activation of the three adjustments principle which triggers the healing adjustment of mind and body, and improves the symbiotic-healing power. Improvement of the symbiotic-healing power helps in the recovery and restoration of ailing organs.

(3) Kiryo Self-Healing: Abdomen (Organs) (10 – 15 Minutes)

First, lay on your back, then check your pulse at your wrist. Next, select either your left or right hand, shape it into the ku-no-ji form, and place it approximately 4 inches away from your abdomen. Do not move it. By doing this, the healing life-energy and the affected organ's energy will be exchanged

After completing all of the above, check your pulse once again. You should notice that it has changed to a composed pulse.

If the organs of your abdomen are ailing in any way, healing life energy exchange will occur between those ailing parts and the palm of your hand. For example, let us say that we have some liver ailment. In such a case, when performing Kiryo, healing life-energy is being exchanged between the palm of our hand and our liver.

Once our liver receives stimulation in the form of healing energy from the palm of our hand, the three healing-adjustments principle begins to take effect, muscular adjustments begin to occur in the liver, blood flow in the liver improves, and the muscle cells become more capable of carrying out cellular respiration.

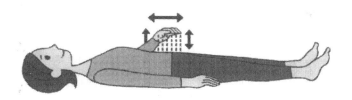

Abdominal (Organ) Self-Healing

Once regenerative metabolism can take place in these cells, the muscles of the liver become soft and supple and their function is improved. Overall, this process is able to assist in the recovery and restoration of the ailing liver.

Additionally, by waving your hand approximately four inches away from other sorts of ailments—including skeletal muscle lacerations, burns, contusions, and broken bones—a degree of pain relief can be achieved, which is nothing but the effect of Kiryo itself.

Chapter 5: Kiryo Partner-Healing

1. Two Life-Energies

At this point, let us again consider the life-energy of our bodies. Humans, plants, and animals live in a natural space suffused with a diverse range of natural energies. I believe that in this natural space, these natural energies are exchanging, intermingling, and unifying with each other. I also believe that the life-energy that we humans, in addition to plants and animals, emit, should be considered one of these natural energies.

Thus, because it is a living Ki *energy*, I will call the life energy that we humans emit during our daily lives "natural life energy." This natural life-energy mingles with that of other creatures like other humans, animals, and birds, but neither we nor they are capable of sensing or reacting to each other's life energy. However, if we were to feel this energy exchange sensation, it would suppress the activity of our cerebrum, inconveniencing us greatly.

But then what about during the healing life energy exchange that takes place in Kiryo exercise or Kiryo healing?

When healing life energy exchange is taking place, it is possible for us to feel the exchange sensation caused by the life energy and affected part energy that is being emitted. Over the last 15 years, I have, in television programs on a number of channels, performed healing life-energy (Ki) exchange with countless animals. Almost all of these animals, upon entering the Kiryo space, relax and contentedly lie down, then slip into a state of Kiryo sleep; which is truly a healing Kiryo slumber.

Thus, I decided to call this healing life energy—a form of healing Ki energy—"Kiryo life energy." In one particular instance, a television station recorded me performing Kiryo life-energy exchange between myself and one hundred geese at a certain zoo.[17]These hundred geese were in an enclosure encircled by a fence. Four staff members and myself entered the enclosure. All five of us were, of course, emitting natural life energy, though the geese still paid us no mind and carried on raucously squawking.

The moment I began to perform Kiryo life-energy exchange (neurotransmissive exchange), the geese, now inside a healing Kiryo space, all simultaneously stopped their squawking, and the area fell silent. Eventually, several of the geese among the flock began to fall into Kiryo sleep: some laying down, and others fell asleep while standing.

The reason the cries of the geese all stopped simultaneously is because the geese perceived my Kiryo life-energy. This perception and differentiation on the part of the geese could be considered proof of Kiryo life-energy itself. It is also proof of the two life-energies we humans possess: the natural life-energy we need to live as well as the Kiryo life-energy we need to heal.

The instance of the geese simultaneously stopping their crying was the first time I had been able to confirm externally the existence of Kiryo life energy. Since then, I've been able to demonstrate such things for a variety of televised programs.

Now let us consider natural life-energy and Kiryo life-energy through the lenses of nervous activity and physiological function.

(1) Natural Life Energy (Living Energy)

We fundamentally rely on the conventional nervous system—as described

---

[17]It is common in Japanese culture to not give specific details about one's past events, and it is also common not to mention branded/copyrighted things—like television program names or broadcast company names—without being given explicit permission from them. This is why Kanzawa is being particularly vague. Because of its benefits to anyone studying Kiryo, there is a list of major events in Tadashi's Author Timeline at the end of the book. The videos of Kanzawa can also greatly improve one's understanding of how to perform Kiryo exercise and what is achievable through Kiryo.

through the efforts of anatomical science—in order to live. The modern brainstem controls modern life functions. Additionally, the modern brainstem is the source of natural healing power as well as the natural life energy we emit in our daily lives.

(2) Kiryo Life Energy (Healing Life Energy)

Phenomenological investigation allows us to examine the true nature (source) of Kiryo life-energy in the Kiryo nervous system centered around the primitive brainstem which lies dormant inside our current, modern brainstem. The primitive brainstem is where the central nerve of the Kiryo nervous system is located. If one heightens and makes use of their Kiryo life-energy through Kiryo exercise, they can awaken their healing sensory functions and primeval life-functions, as well as elevate their symbiotic healing powers, and eventually master all of them. In other words, one can improve and master their symbiotic healing power (lessen the suppressive function of the cerebrum).

2. Kiryo Partner-Healing

Let us consider the healing neurotransmission that occurs between the Kiryo practitioner and the Kiryo recipient from the perspective of the Kiryo nervous system.

(1) The Kiryo Practitioner: Internal Neurotransmissive Exchange vs. Body-External Neurotransmissive Exchange

The Kiryo practitioner begins performing Kiryo healing on the Kiryo recipient using their five-fingered ku-no-ji palm (ancient palm).

The moment the Kiryo practitioner attempts to feel the Kiryo recipient's life-energies (natural life energy and Kiryo life energy) and affected part energy, his or her cerebrum's normal suppressive function is lessened. As long as the

124

Kiryo practitioner is engaging in *feel as you are* Kiryo life-energy exchange with the Kiryo recipient using their ku-no-ji palm, the suppressive functions of the cerebrum will remain in a mitigated state.

While this is taking place, two sorts of neurotransmissions occur in the nervous system of the Kiryo practitioner. The first is neurotransmission within his or her body, and the second is neurotransmission with another (outside the body). As I have already discussed both of these neurotransmissions, I will omit a detailed explanation of their particulars here.

(2) What the Kiryo Practitioner Should Keep in Mind during Partner-Healing

While performing Kiryo partner-healing, or Kiryo healing in general, please be aware of the following:

1. The *Ku no ji* Palm Must be *Feeling as It Is.*

Placing the five-fingered ku-no-ji palm into a *feel as you are* state is the one and only way of entering the world of Kiryo. This "feeling as you are" state forces the normal suppressive function of the cerebrum into a mitigated state, and so catalyzes a switch in the Kiryo practitioner from the cognitive world (cognitive side) to the sensory world (sensory side).

After the five fingers have been assembled together in the ku-no-ji palm, please do not try to actively move them. Attempting to move your fingers disturbs the "feeling as you are" state; which causes the cerebrum to return to its normal suppressive functionality—that is, its normal cognitive processes. Consequently, the Kiryo effects of partner healing are destroyed. *Feeling as you are* is the cornerstone of Kiryo practice. While our daily lives are conducted with the oversight of the cognitive side of our brains, the sensory side of things, through the "feeling as you are" state of the five-fingered ku-no-ji palm (ancient palm), reigns supreme.

2. The Perception and Differentiation of the *Ku-no-ji Palm*

125

(Perceptive Differentiation and Sensory Stiffening Nerves)

The Kiryo practitioner perceives and differentiates the life energies (natural life energy and healing life energy) and affected part energy of the Kiryo recipient with their ku-no-ji palm and their Kiryo nerves. Categorization of that perceptive and differentiative ability is based on criteria pertaining to two phenomena. The first set of criteria pertain to the feedback sensation, and the second set to the hand form.

(A) Criteria for the Hand Feedback Sensation (Perceptive Differentiation Nerve)

The hand feedback sensation is a sensation in the Kiryo practitioner caused by their perceptive differentiation nerve. These sensations vary from person to person, so I'll provide three simple criteria to enable you to categorize your own hand feedback sensation.

I. The strength or weakness of the hand feedback sensation is relative to the strength of the change in the Kiryo recipient's life-energies or affected part energy. As the affected part of the Kiryo recipient is recovered, its affected part energy will weaken, and the hand feedback sensation experienced by the Kiryo practitioner will also weaken.

II. The Type of Hand Feedback Sensations (Sensory Words and Terms) The type of hand feedback sensation felt by the Kiryo practitioner upon encountering the life energies and affected part energy of the Kiryo recipient will vary from person to person. Please examine *Figure 3: Types of Hand Feedback Sensations at a Glance.*

III. The Hardness or Softness of the Hand Feedback Sensation is determined by the nature of the change in the life energies and the affected part energy of the Kiryo recipient. As the affected part of the Kiryo recipient is recovered, this affected part energy will soften, and the hand feedback sensation of the Kiryo practitioner will also soften.

The above three criteria for categorizing the nature of one's hand feedback sensation should allow the Kiryo practitioner to grasp, albeit somewhat dimly, the recovery of the injuries and illnesses suffered by the Kiryo recipient.

(B) The Reason the Kiryo Practitioner Does Not Notice Their Hand Stiffening in One of Three Hand Forms

When the Kiryo practitioner performs Kiryo healing on a recipient, they are making use of the five-fingered ku-no-ji palm. The Kiryo practitioner's ku-no-ji palm, in response to the strength or weakness of the change in the life-energies and affected part energy of the Kiryo recipient, undergoes sensory stiffening by the action of the sensory stiffening nerve. This sensory stiffening causes the ku-no-ji palm to adopt one of three possible hand *forms*.

Please examine Figure 8 on page 96: *Figure 8: The Ku no Ji Palm: The Protocol* (Feedback Sensation). Pay special attention to items 8 and 9 in the "Sensory Stiffening Nerve" column.

When the Kiryo practitioner is exposed to the stimuli of the life-energies and affected part energy of the Kiryo recipient, the strength or lack thereof of that stimulus will cause the ku-no-ji palm to assume one of three forms, as described in item 8.

O The ku-no-ji palm *undergoes sensory stiffness as it is*

For almost all Kiryo practitioners, the ku-no-ji palm experiences sensory stiffness unchanged, remaining in the ku-no-ji form.

O The ku-no-ji palm *undergoes sensory stiffness in the shape of a clenched fist*

When the affected part energy of the Kiryo recipient is especially strong, the Kiryo practitioner's *ku no ji* palm naturally assumes the shape of a clenched fist.

O The fingers of the ku-no-ji palm *each undergo sensory stiffness in* some *modified*

127

position

The five fingers of the ku-no-ji palm of the Kiryo practitioner may undergo sensory stiffening in some modified, open position that varies from practitioner to practitioner.

Thus, in accordance with the strength or weakness of the change in the affected part energy of the Kiryo recipient, the ku-no-ji palm of the Kiryo practitioner will, via the activity of the sensory stiffening nerve, undergo sensory stiffening and become one of the three hand forms. However, it is rare that the Kiryo practitioner will notice their palms undergoing sensory stiffening in these three forms.

Why is that? The healing sensory function, which senses life-energies and affected part energy, is normally sealed away by the suppressive function of the cerebrum. At the same time, just like autonomic nervous function, healing sensory function is governed by the brainstem, so we cannot actively sense it.

When a Kiryo recipient's affected part is recovered, its affected part energy is extinguished, meaning that the three possible hand forms resulting from sensory stiffening of the Kiryo practitioner's ku-no-ji palm also disappear. Simply put, the three sensory stiffening forms of the Kiryo practitioner's ku-no-ji palm can detect the condition of the Kiryo recipient's affected part. As is indicated in item 9, the ability to differentiate various types of energy via the ku-no-ji palm becomes possible. This is an incontrovertible fact.

(C) The Methods of Kiryo Partner-Healing: Hand-Waving and Stillness

Kiryo healing refers to the Kiryo practitioner performing hand-waving and stillness with their five-fingered ku-no-ji palm to treat injuries and illnesses in a Kiryo recipient. The practitioner will use whatever hand is Ki-dominant— the hand that is more strongly able to feel the hand feedback sensation—to perform Kiryo healing.

I have performed Kiryo healing on recipients using many different methods, but to this day, none have been able to match the effectiveness of hand-waving and stillness. Therefore, we'll be focusing on this method and discussing its roles and functions.

I.   Waving of the *Ku-no-ji* Palm

Waving of the *ku no ji* palm uses Kiryo life-energy to stimulate the Kiryo nervous system and the conventional nervous system in a Kiryo recipient. The nervous systems of the Kiryo recipient are vitalized by the stimulation caused by hand-waving.

II.   Stillness of the *Ku-no-ji Palm*

Stillness of the *ku no ji* palm involves using the hand feedback sensation to perceive and differentiate the recovery and restoration of the affected part of the Kiryo recipient. However, for perception and differentiation (however vague) to become possible, one must diligently practice other-person Kiryo healing.

3   The Fundamental Techniques and the Structure of Kiryo Partner

Now we'll examine the fundamental methods of Kiryo partner-healing using illustrated examples.

1: Checking the Pulse at the Wrist

The pulse is one's metric for tracking the recovery of illness and injury. In Kiryo, it is very important that we check the rhythm and beating pattern of the pulse before beginning Kiryo healing. It allows us to confirm the manifestation of the three adjustments principle.

Checking the pulse of an individual suffering from a chronic illness

129

should tell you that their average blood flow is low, and that their blood vessels have become quite narrow.

When a Kiryo practitioner attempts to check the pulse of the Kiryo recipient, they should bring their pointer finger, middle finger, and ring finger together and lay all three of them on the recipient's wrist. Then, by angling his or her nails toward the wrist, one should be able to feel the location of the recipient's blood vessel (artery). It is simple enough to check the pulse from there on. Be sure to note blood flow, the plumpness of the blood vessel, and the degree of expansion and contraction (normal beating pattern) that occurs over one beat.

Note: The rate of the pulse varies from person to person, and we shall therefore not pay too much attention to it.

Checking the Pulse at the Wrist (Before Kiryo)

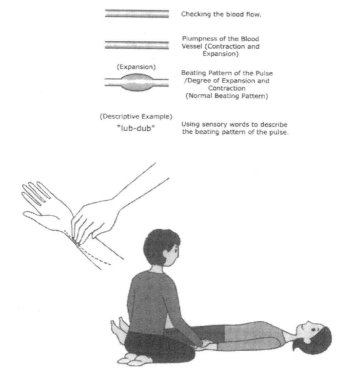

Checking the blood flow.

Plumpness of the Blood
Vessel (Contraction and
Expansion)

(Expansion)

Beating Pattern of the Pulse
/Degree of Expansion and
Contraction
(Normal Beating Pattern)

(Descriptive Example)
"lub-dub"

Using sensory words to describe
the beating pattern of the pulse.

Kiryo Healing of the Head: Awakening the Primitive Brainstem

(the Wholesome Brainstem)

The Kiryo practitioner takes the five-fingered ku-no-ji palm of their Ki-dominant hand and performs Kiryo healing on the crown and both sides of the Kiryo recipient's head (refer to the illustration on the next page). The Kiryo practitioner should keep their hand in a still state about four inches away from the Kiryo recipient's head and, from there, perceive and differentiate (perceptive differentiation nerve) its energy.

Next, the Kiryo practitioner moves their *ku no ji* palm up and down with respect to the head, as well as to the front and sides of the head, to perform hand-waving. This hand-waving stimulates the cells of the Kiryo

131

recipient's brain (central nerves).

As the energies of the Kiryo recipient's cerebrum, brainstem, and cerebellum grow stronger, sensory stiffening (sensory stiffening nerve) will begin to occur in the ku-no-ji palm of the Kiryo practitioner. The stronger that energy gets, the form of the Kiryo practitioner's ku-no-ji palm will, due to orders from the brainstem, adopt either an unchanged ku-no-ji shape, a clenched fist shape, or another modified shape and continue to undergo sensory stiffening (the criteria of perception and differentiation).

Healing Corporal Effects in the Kiryo Recipient: Blood is Brought to the Brainstem, and Proper Regenerative Metabolism Occurs

Due to the practitioner's hand-waving, the Kiryo recipient's brain (cerebrum, brainstem, and cerebellum) is stimulated, and blood is brought to it. This blood ensures that nutrients and oxygen are being sufficiently provided to the brain, that waste products are being properly carried away, and allows for proper regenerative metabolism to occur.

The brain is vitalized when we relax. In the brain of the Kiryo recipient, perhaps because sleep substances are sent from the brainstem to the cerebrum, the Kiryo recipient will find it quite easy to slip into Kiryo sleep.

Kiryo Healing of the Head (About 5 Minutes)

132

Kiryo sleep is like normal sleep, a function of the parasympathetic nerves that rests the cerebrum, removes fatigue from the body, and heals illnesses and injuries. Furthermore, the vitalized wholesome brainstem (unification of the primitive brainstem and the modern brainstem) sends strong orders to live throughout the body (skeletal muscles and visceral muscles, etc.) via the sensory stiffening nerve and the autonomic nerves, and brings about the three adjustments principle.

As the three adjustments principle comes into effect, the amount of blood reaching the brain increases. Simultaneously, vascular adjustment of the brain's blood vessels occurs, and their contractions and expansions grow larger. Consequently, the vessels fatten and become elastic, and the flow of blood through them becomes composed. In other words, this process acts against and prevents stroke-like illnesses such as cerebral hemorrhages, cerebral infarct, and subarachnoid hemorrhage.

After being stimulated by the hand-waving of the *ku no ji* palm of the Kiryo practitioner, the modern brainstem receives proper and sufficient nutrients and oxygen, and so is vitalized. Further, the primitive brainstem, which lies dormant as genetic information inside the modern brainstem, is awoken, and it unifies with the modern brainstem to become the wholesome brainstem.

The wholesome brainstem unifies the Kiryo nervous system and the conventional nervous system, carries out the three adjustments principle and healing adjustment of mind and body, improves self-healing power, and manifests the Kiryo effects of recovery and restoration from illness. Additionally, the partner-healing power of the Kiryo recipient is also heightened.

Kiryo Healing of the Heart: Cardiac Adjustment/Vascular Adjustment (Coronary Arteries)

The Kiryo practitioner takes the five-fingered ku-no-ji palm of their Ki-dominant hand and performs Kiryo healing on the Kiryo recipient's heart (refer to the illustration on the next page). The Kiryo practitioner should keep their hand in a still state about four inches away from the Kiryo recipient's heart and, from there, perceive and differentiate its energy.

133

Next, the Kiryo practitioner moves their ku-no-ji palm side-to-side to perform hand-waving. This hand-waving stimulates the nerves of the Kiryo recipient's heart. As the energy of the Kiryo recipient's heart grows stronger after being thus stimulated, sensory stiffening will begin to occur in the ku-no-ji palm of the Kiryo practitioner (sensory stiffening nerve).

The stronger that energy gets, the form of Kiryo practitioner's ku-no-ji palm will, due to orders from the brainstem, undergo sensory stiffening into the same hand form it did during the healing of the head (the criteria of perception and differentiation). The Kiryo practitioner will stimulate the nerves of the heart of the Kiryo recipient while hand-waving, and by stilling their hand, will perceive and differentiate the change in the heart's energy.

Kiryo Healing of the Heart (About 2 Minutes)

Healing Corporal Effects in the Kiryo Recipient: Cardiac and Vascular Adjustment Strengthens Cardiac Function

Through the hand-waving of the Kiryo practitioner's ku-no-ji palm, the nerves of the heart in the Kiryo recipient are stimulated, and cardiac function is vitalized. Consequently, by activity of the sensory stiffening nerve, sustained instantaneous stiffening of the muscles occurs in the heart of the Kiryo recipient.

134

Via this continued instantaneous stiffening, the contractions and expansions of the cardiac muscles become larger as well as becoming more elastic. This is called *cardiac adjustment*.

Alongside cardiac adjustment, the contractions and expansions of the blood vessels (coronary arteries) become larger, and the vessels themselves also grow fatter and softer. This is called *vascular adjustment*. Cardiac adjustment and vascular adjustment (of the coronary arteries) combine to strengthen cardiac function.

Both cardiac adjustment and vascular adjustment occur because of the activity of the sensory stiffening nerve. This activity can be visualized by likening it to strengthening the wringing of a soaked towel.

Further, the sensory stiffening nerve is capable of effecting muscular adjustment in all the muscles and vessels of the body. This causes the contractions and expansions of the body's blood vessels to grow larger and, as a result, become fatter and softer—checking the pulse at the wrist should help you to observe this. The blood inside these vessels should flow composedly, firmly, and strongly. This good and proper blood circulation causes blood flow to enter a "composed pulse" state, and internal respiration to enter a "composed breathing" state. Additionally, good and proper blood circulation causes healing adjustment of body and mind, and overall improves symbiotic healing power.

Furthermore, it is particularly good at manifesting Kiryo effects in the conditions of angina pectoris or myocardial infarction and helps to prevent these illnesses as well.

I was once told the story of a man's mother, and how she was revived from a critical, near-death state. His mother's blood pressure had fallen considerably, and she was on the verge of death. He placed his hand on her chest and called to her. At that moment, the man apparently felt in the hand he had placed on his mother's chest a tingling, electric sensation. Immediately after, his mother's blood pressure began to rise, and she soon revived.

What are we to think of this incident?

Kiryo theory would surmise that the life energy (Kiryo life energy) being emitted from that man's Kiryo nervous system stimulated the nerves of his mother's heart. When we speak of the nerves of the mother's heart, we are primarily referring to the perceptive differentiation nerve, the sensory stiffening nerve, and the autonomic nerves. When these three nerves are

135

stimulated, the three adjustments principle is activated, cardiac adjustment and vascular adjustment are carried out, and cardiac function is recovered and restored.

Kiryo Healing of the Lower Abdomen (About three minutes)

Kiryo Healing of the Lower Abdomen: Digestive Organs, Excretory Organs, and Reproductive Organs

Our focus here is the pit of the stomach, which refers to the part of one's lower abdomen that lies below the belly button. It is said that by strengthening this part of one's body, they can gain health and courage.

In Kiryo, we focus on its application to the visceral muscles: those of the digestive tract, of the excretory system, and of the reproductive organs. The functions of these different systems are as follows: the digestive organs absorb nutrients; the excretory organs eliminate waste products from within the body; and the reproductive organs allow for the birth of new life.

The Kiryo practitioner takes the five-fingered ku-no-ji palm of their Ki-dominant hand and performs Kiryo healing on the visceral muscles of

136

the Kiryo recipient's lower abdomen. The Kiryo practitioner should, as he or she did during healing of the heart, keep their hand in a still state about four inches away from the Kiryo recipient's lower abdomen and from there perceive and differentiate the energy of its visceral muscles.

Next, the Kiryo practitioner moves their ku-no-ji palm side-to-side to perform hand-waving. This stimulates the nerves of the recipient's organs. As the energy of the Kiryo recipient's internal organs grow stronger after being thus stimulated, sensory stiffening will begin to occur in the ku-no-ji palm of the Kiryo practitioner (sensitive rigidity nerve). The Kiryo practitioner will stimulate the nerves of the internal organs of the Kiryo recipient while hand-waving and, by also stilling their hand when appropriate, will perceive and differentiate the change in the heart's energy.

The nerves of the internal organs of the Kiryo recipient, being thus stimulated by the hand-waving of the Kiryo practitioner's ku-no-ji palm, will cause a vitalization of the sensory stiffening nerve and the autonomic nerves, and the function of the internal organs will increase.

Healing Corporal Effects in the Kiryo Recipient: The Nerves of the Lower Abdomen Will Be Stimulated, and the Functions of the Various Internal Organs will be Vitalized

By the hand-waving of the Kiryo practitioner's ku-no-ji palm, the nerves in the organs of the lower abdomen of the Kiryo recipient are stimulated. This stimulation of these nerves vitalizes the functions of the small intestine, large intestine, kidneys, appendix, uterus, ovaries, and other various organs. Consequently, by activity of the stimulated sensitive rigidity nerve, sustained instantaneous stiffening occurs in the muscles of the various internal organs of the Kiryo recipient.

The muscular adjustment caused by this sustained instantaneous stiffening widens the breadth of the contractions and relaxations of the muscles of the internal organs, and the three adjustments principle is activated. After the three adjustments principle is activated, digestive function, internal purification function, and reproductive function are all vitalized.

The three adjustments principle is particularly effective at bringing about Kiryo effects on gynecological ailments. For example, in the case of

137

ovarian cysts, once blood flow is strengthened through contractions and relaxations, the cyst is expelled as a foreign body.

In the case of a uterine myoma, as the contractions and relaxations of the uterus become stronger, a sort of wringing motion results. This wringing motion begins to expel the myoma, and as a result, the myoma shrinks.

Because gynecological problems (activity of the parasympathetic nervous system) result from abnormalities in reproductive organs that are directly tied to the brainstem, Kiryo effects can be manifested on ailments like menstrual pain, irregular menstruation, amenorrhea, and infertility.

Kiryo Healing with the Soles of the Feet

When it comes to our feet, even though the sensations we can feel are faint, their power to emit Kiryo life-energy and stimulate the nerves of the Kiryo recipient is still several times that of the ku-no-ji palm. I have deduced this fact from the testimonials of many Kiryo recipients.

The method for Kiryo partner-healing with the feet is as follows. The Kiryo practitioner sits with the sole of one of their feet about 4 inches away from the sole of the Kiryo recipient's feet as they lie on their back. Even if the Kiryo practitioner cannot feel anything, Kiryo healing has already begun (see illustration on the next page).

The Kiryo life-energy of the Kiryo practitioner, transmits strong stimuli from the soles of the feet through the capillary nerves and up to the brain (central nerves) of the Kiryo recipient. The Kiryo practitioner, regardless of whether or not they feel or does not feel anything, should remain still and not move their foot. They should also *feel as they are* and *be as they are.*

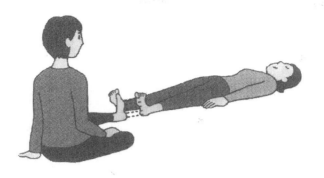

Kiryo Healing of the Soles of the Feet (About 10 Minutes)

While this is taking place, the nerves of the Kiryo recipient are receiving Kiryo life-energy stimulation from the Kiryo practitioner. That stimulus is transmitted from the capillary nerves of the soles of the feet, then to the peripheral nerves (spinal nerves, cranial nerves, Kiryo nerves), and finally up to the central nerves (cerebrum, brainstem, and cerebellum). The life-energies (natural life energy and Kiryo life energy) and affected part energy of the Kiryo recipient are transmitted from the capillary nerves in the soles of the feet of the Kiryo practitioner to their peripheral nerves and up to their central nerves. Both parties are stimulating each other.

Both people are engaging in exchange and transmission that stimulates their Kiryo nervous systems. This is body-external neurotransmission, that is, neurotransmission with another person: contrary to what might be thought possible in conventional medical knowledge.

In our daily lives, the normal suppressive function of the cerebrum hinders this ability, but when that suppressive function is mitigated, neurotransmission with another person can occur from sole-to-sole. This is evidence that the foot's feedback sensation is dull but exists nonetheless.

During sole-to-sole healing, both Kiryo practitioner and Kiryo recipient must not move their legs, and they must *be as they are* and *feel as they are* to perform healing neurotransmissive exchange. This is also healing neurostimulatory exchange. However, the Kiryo recipient may, due to the activity of the sensitive rigidity nerve, experience their hands or feet moving

139

(manifest stiffening).

I urge all readers to try sole-to-sole Kiryo healing. I suspect a great many people who suffer from chronic illnesses will be able to feel Kiryo life-energy through the soles of their feet.

Healing Corporal Effects in the Kiryo Recipient: Stimulation of the Soles of the Feet Will Awaken the Primitive Brainstem, and Lead to Recovery of Illness and Injury

As far as Kiryo partner-healing is concerned, the practice of using the soles of the feet to perform Kiryo healing on the soles of the feet of the Kiryo recipient is indispensable. This is because a strong Kiryo life-energy, rooted in the Kiryo nervous system, is emitted from the soles of the feet. That strong Kiryo life-energy of the Kiryo practitioner stimulates the nerves in the sole of the foot of the Kiryo recipient. This stimulation is transmitted to the brain. In particular, it stimulates the brainstem, and awakens the primitive brainstem.

Kiryo Healing of Affected Parts: When There Are Many Affected Parts, or When One Must Heighten Weakened Stamina

When I began doing Kiryo partner-healing, the practice only involved using the *ku no ji* palm to perform Kiryo healing on the affected parts of the Kiryo recipient. I had adopted the Kiryo healing technique of holding the *ku no ji* palm about four inches from the affected part of the Kiryo recipient, then waving it left and right, keeping it still, and *feeling as I* was.

That method has not changed, and I believe I will continue to use it. Kiryo partner-healing is exceedingly simple, and yet it still brings about wonderful Kiryo effects.

Sometime later, however, I realized that a method that only performs Kiryo healing on affected parts has two main problems. The first is what to do in the event that there are multiple illnesses or injuries? The second, is what to do to in order to heighten weakened stamina (life force)?

In an effort to solve these two problems, I attempted, through trial and error, many different techniques. As a result, I realized that these problems could be solved through separate Kiryo healing of the head (brain), the heart, the lower abdomen, and the soles of the feet.

Kiryo healing of the head heightens the life force and battles with illness, and therefore I looked for its Kiryo effects in the brainstem in particular. Kiryo healing of the heart creates an improvement in blood circulation throughout the body. Kiryo healing of the lower abdomen brings an improvement to the function of the internal organs. Kiryo healing through the soles of the feet brings about stimulation of the capillary nerves of the feet up to the central nerves of the brain. Thus, Kiryo healing of the head (brain), heart, lower abdomen, and through the soles of the feet work together to bring about the Kiryo effects of recovery and restoration on the affected part (illness or injury).

The moment the Kiryo practitioner begins Kiryo healing with his or her five-fingered *ku no ji* palm on the affected part of the Kiryo recipient, the suppressive function of the brainstem is lessened, and the Kiryo nervous system centered around the primitive brainstem begins to activate. Kiryo life energy, rooted in the Kiryo nervous system, is emitted from the *ku no ji* palm of the Kiryo practitioner.

This Kiryo life energy stimulates the nerves of the affected part of the Kiryo recipient. This stimulation of the nerves begins the recovery and restoration of the affected part, and its affected part energy begins to change. The ku no ji palm of the Kiryo practitioner can perceive and differentiate this change in the affected part energy through the perceptive differentiation nerve and the sensitive rigidity nerve.

Because the affected part of the Kiryo recipient is recovered and restored, its affected part energy is extinguished, the twitching, tingling, and stiffening hand feedback sensations in the ku-no-ji palm of the Kiryo practitioner also recede.

141

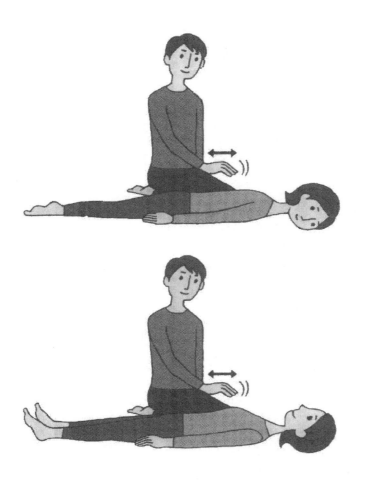

Kiryo Healing of the Affected Part (About 20-30 Minutes)

142

When the pain of an affected part is particularly severe, or in other exigent circumstances, Kiryo healing must be performed on the affected part immediately. As a rule of thumb, the Kiryo practitioner will perform Kiryo healing on the Kiryo recipient's head (brain), heart, lower abdomen, and soles of the feet in turn. After that, he or she will perform Kiryo healing on the affected part.

Re-Checking of the Pulse at the Wrist: A Composed Pulse Indicates that Internal Respiration is Occurring

As other-person Kiryo healing begins, the three adjustments principle is simultaneously activated in the Kiryo recipient. That is, muscular adjustment caused by sustained instantaneous stiffening, blood flow adjustment caused by the cardiac and vascular adjustment brought about by sustained instantaneous contraction (contraction and expansion), and internal respiration—that is, respiratory adjustment brought about by cellular respiration—all begin. As this three adjustments principle is activated, the healing adjustment of body and mind is carried out.

How does the pulse of the Kiryo recipient, after Kiryo healing, differ from their pulse before? Please examine the illustration titled, "Re-Checking of the Pulse at the Wrist." Let us check the pulse of the Kiryo recipient at the wrist in the way indicated.

Before Kiryo healing, blood flow will be ordinary, flow rate will be ordinary, the expansion and elongation associated with each beat will be ordinary, and the pulse will sound similar to, "lub-dub."

After Kiryo healing, however, blood flow will be good and proper, the vessels will be plumper due to broader contractions and expansions, the elongation associated with each beat will be greater, and an extending of each beat, similar to, "luubb-duubb," will be heard. In Kiryo, this pattern of beating is described as composed, firm, strong, plump, and soft.

"Composed", "firm", and "strong" signify the good and proper nature of the blood circulation, and "plump" and "soft" signify the fact that the blood vessels have grown plump: their contractions and expansions have grown broader. These terms also indicate that the muscles of the heart have acquired an elastic quality. Thus, the heart and the blood vessels have become

143

elastic, and blood circulation has become good and proper. All of these changes signify that the function of the circulatory system, centered around the heart, has improved.

I would especially like to emphasize the changes that have occurred to the nature of each beat of the pulse. Using the three fingers, examine the pulse as described on page 131. The Kiryo practitioner should be able to confirm that the pulsating vessel's expansions, and the blood passing through it, have both increased. Next, one should be able to confirm the elongation of the vessel; in other words, the fact that the pulse has become deeper and longer. If one were to feel the pulse before Kiryo healing as "lub-dub", the change in the depth and length of the pulse following Kiryo healing could be represented by "luubb-duubb".

This "luubb-duubb" representation holds a very important meaning in the context of Kiryo theory. This is because the continued "luubb-duubb" pattern signifies the composed pulse, meaning that muscular adjustment and blood flow adjustment have indeed occurred. Further, it signifies that internal respiration—cellular respiration/respiratory adjustments proceeding vigorously.

When internal respiration—cellular respiration— has been restored, the inhalations and exhalations of external respiration become much easier. So, both internal and external respiration both become *composed respiration*.

Rechecking the Pulse at the Wrist
(After Treatment)

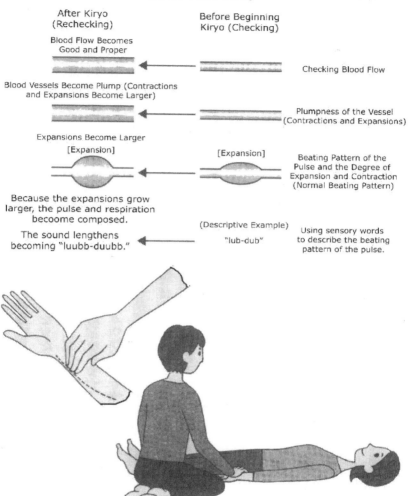

After Kiryo
(Rechecking)

Before Beginning
Kiryo (Checking)

Blood Flow Becomes
Good and Proper

Checking Blood Flow

Blood Vessels Become Plump (Contractions
and Expansions Become Larger)

Plumpness of the Vessel
(Contractions and Expansions)

Expansions Become Larger

[Expansion]

[Expansion]

Beating Pattern of the
Pulse and the Degree of
Expansion and Contraction
(Normal Beating Pattern)

Because the expansions grow
larger, the pulse and respiration
becoome composed.

The sound lengthens
becoming "luubb-duubb."

(Descriptive Example)

"lub-dub"

Using sensory words
to describe the beating
pattern of the pulse.

145

People suffering from chronic illnesses tend to keep their entire bodies (skeletal and visceral muscles) in a very tense state, and therefore mostly breathe with the help of their chest and/or shoulders. Yet, composed respiration naturally becomes abdominal respiration.

From the perspective of nervous activity, a composed pulse and composed respiration are both due to the activity of the sensory stiffening nerve and the parasympathetic nerves (autonomic nerves).

Unlike the hurried pulse caused by the oxygen demands created during sports and exercise, the beat of a composed pulse is the slow beat of healing-focused, good and proper blood circulation. This type of circulation supplies nutrients and oxygen to each cell, removes waste products, and carries out regenerative metabolism.

The cells of the brain and the nerves are particularly receptive to this provision of nutrients and oxygen and are vitalized by it. This allows the Kiryo and conventional nervous systems to unify, and body-internal neurotransmission becomes restored. As well, the sensory stiffening nerve and the parasympathetic nerves (autonomic nerves) are activated.

Thus, the composed pulse seen in Kiryo recipients during Kiryo partner-healing helps bring about healing adjustment of body and mind, and manifest the Kiryo effects of recovery and restoration on parts of the body affected by illness and injury. As a result, one's self- and partner-healing powers are improved and amplified.

(D) Hand-Waving: An Experience-Based Rule

When a Kiryo practitioner performs partner-healing, the process appears very simple. After all, the practitioner simply performs hand-waving from to side-to-side with one five-fingered ku-no-ji palm (either the left or the right) about four inches away from the patient's body and its affected parts.

One might ask, "Why the hand-waving?"

Hand-waving is an experience-based technique (empirical law) that has proven to be incredibly effective after years of practice.

Countless so-called miracles, considered impossible through the lens

146

of conventional medicine and science, have been performed by hand-waving the ku-no-ji palm. These all involved the miraculous restoration and recovery of illnesses and injuries. It was similarly "miraculous" when, in the various television programs both inside and outside Japan that I have participated in over the last ten years, animals fell into Kiryo sleep (perhaps some of you have seen these programs).[18]

It was the hand-waving of my (right) ku-no-ji palm that made these animals fall into Kiryo sleep. Though, before the instances mentioned above, it was exceedingly difficult to theoretically prove why hand-waving was so capable of bringing about Kiryo effects.

3. Kiryo Healing for Pets

Nowadays, it is common to have pets. And, just as humans suffer from illnesses and injuries, so too do pets. After all, animals are living things, so this is to be expected. Consequently, I would assume that many of us would find it convenient if we were able to perform Kiryo healing on the injuries and illnesses of dogs, birds, and other pets. And, in addition, if Kiryo healing could prevent them from getting sick, all the better.

In that vein, let us consider the differences between animals and humans. In humans, the suppressive function of the cerebrum has sealed away the sensory function that senses Kiryo life energy. For most, only our ku-no-ji palms and soles are initially capable of faintly detecting this sensation.

However, animals depend primarily, as proven by anatomical investigations in modern medical science, on a nervous system centered around the brainstem to live. Considering the phenomena of Kiryo, it is apparent that these animals (dogs, cats, birds, and other animals) also live by relying on the Kiryo nervous system centered around the primitive brainstem. Consequently, we know that animals possess strong primeval life functions and strong healing sensory functions.

The healing sensory function of animals, which is responsible for sensing Kiryo life energy, is anywhere from several hundred to several thousand times stronger than the healing sensory function of the human ku-

---

[18] See Author Profile at end of book for list of television programs.

no-ji palm.

It is often said that animals have a strong life force and having a strong life force means that their self-healing power, which combats injury and illness, is strong. However, because they live comfortably alongside humans, pets may have weaker life forces than those of wild animals. Yet still, their self-healing power should be stronger than that of a human. This means that, more so than on humans, Kiryo healing will be spectacularly effective on dogs, cats, birds, and other pets. Therefore, it is important for pet owners to become Kiryo practitioners and perform Kiryo healing on their beloved pets.

The nature of the corporal healing effects of Kiryo healing on pets is the same as what occurs in humans. Chapter 5, which discusses Kiryo partner-healing [beginning on page 121], may provide helpful insight.

(1) Experimenting with Neurotransmissive Exchange on Pets (A Proof)

Please look at the illustrations depicting neurotransmissive exchange with dogs and cats shown on the next page.

Shape your hand (right or left) into the five-fingered ku-no-ji form. The distance between you and your pet should be 3 to 5 meters. However, this will still work if you are further away.

First, keep your hand in the ku-no-ji shape and feel the life-energy of the dog or the cat, etc. Whether you feel it or not, neurotransmissive exchange has already begun. Start waving your ku-no-ji palm side-to-side.

The pet may react to your hand in ku-no-ji shape, or to the Kiryo life energy, and may act differently. If you observe any unusual movements, it is a form of proof that Kiryo life-energy exchange is in act via neurotransmissive exchange.

Continue hand-waving, making sure to punctuate the movement with periods of stillness.

Neurotransmissive exchange with dogs and cats — first, from a place where you can see each other, perform hand-waving (the upper picture). Next, place an object in between to hide your hand-waving from the pets (the lower picture). This will work even when you are further away from them.

Next, the Kiryo practitioner (pet owner) should place something in front of themselves to prevent their hand-waving from being seen. Or one can also hide behind something to achieve the same effect. Then perform the same act you have done in ①. Try doing it from outside the room.

Once the Kiryo practitioner has begun hand-waving, if the pet raises its ears or begins to look around curiously, then we can be sure that neurotransmissive exchange caused by Kiryo life-energy exchange is occurring. In other words, this will be proof that Kiryo life-energy, originating in the Kiryo nervous system (and neurotransmissive exchange, which stimulates the Kiryo nervous system) is occurring between the Kiryo practitioner (pet owner) and the pet.

Neurotransmissive exchange is a healing procedure for pets, so please perform it repeatedly.

(2) Kiryo Healing of Pets: Neurotransmissive Exchange

Countless kinds of animals, birds, and fish are kept as pets. One time, when my goldfish was about to die and was lying on his side in his tank, I performed hand-waving with my ku-no-ji palm on him, and he became lively and energetic again. Pets and humans are both living things, and therefore both have nerve systems. When a Kiryo practitioner (human) performs Kiryo healing on their injuries and illnesses, our beloved pets experience the Kiryo effects of recovery and restoration. As mentioned, the Kiryo effects on pets will be much greater than on humans. I have heard from Kiryo practitioners, Kiryo Academy students, and even those with nearly no Kiryo experience that their pets' illnesses and injuries were recovered and restored through Kiryo healing.

Kiryo Healing of the Head and Spine of Dogs and Cats: Lying on their Belly

The Kiryo practitioner (pet owner) sends Kiryo life-energy, which originates in the Kiryo nervous system, through their five-fingered ku-no-ji palm, while performing hand-waving, into the nerves of the head and spine of a dog or cat that is lying on its belly. This is Kiryo healing of the head (brain) and spine (spinal cord). You may use one hand to cradle the animal to help with positioning. It is also can be helpful to perform this exchange with the pet on one's lap.

Corporal Healing Effects in Dogs and Cats: The Brainstem is Stimulated, and They Fall into a Kiryo Sleep

Unlike humans, whose cerebra possess a suppressive faculty, pets like dogs and cats are primarily brainstem-driven animals. However, because they live alongside humans in a comfortable environment, their brainstems have become quite latent. As a result, the hand-waving and stillness of the ku-no-ji palm of the Kiryo practitioner will stimulate the latent brainstem of the dog or cat.

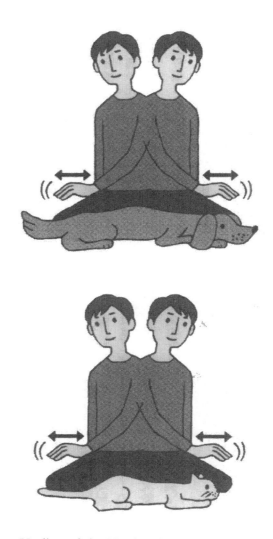

Kiryo Healing of the Head and Spine of Dogs or Cats

When their brainstems are activated, the dog or cat achieves restored blood circulation, and nutrients and oxygen are then provided to their brainstem: vitalizing it. In other words, the hand-waving of the Kiryo practitioner's ku-no-ji palm calls forth blood, pumped towards the brain which massages the brain cells. As a result, the animals relax and slip into a healing Kiryo-sleep.

This is how the primitive brainstem is awakened and the orders to heal sickness or wounds are then transmitted throughout the body by the nerves.

As many know, we have a spinal cord inside our spines. Our spinal cord is a very important nerve that connects the central nerves (the brain) with the peripheral nerves. In Kiryo, the spinal cord is referred to as the intersection of the nerves. The Kiryo practitioner (the owner of the animal) performs Kiryo healing on the brain (head) and spinal cord (spine) of the animal.

Kiryo Healing of the Belly and Four Legs of Dogs and Cats: Lying on their Side

The Kiryo practitioner sends Kiryo life-energy through their ku-no-ji palm while performing hand-waving into the nerves of the belly and four legs of a dog or cat that is sleeping on its side. This is Kiryo healing of the belly and four legs. A practitioner may use one hand to cradle the animal. It is also permissible to perform this exchange with one's pet on one's lap.

Corporal Healing Effects in Dogs and Cats: Kiryo Effects on Illness and Injury

The Kiryo practitioner stimulates the belly of their cat or dog while it is lying on its side by performing hand-waving with their ku-no-ji palm. When doing so, please attempt to stimulate all of the pet's organ's nerves near the heart.

By stimulating all of the organs in the abdomen, the three adjustments principle (muscular adjustment, blood flow adjustment, and respiratory adjustment), immune adjustment, hormonal adjustment, body

153

temperature adjustment, and mental adjustment, among others, are carried out, and self-healing ability is also heightened. As well, there are Kiryo effects against organ illnesses. Additionally, by stimulating the part of the pet's four legs affected by illness or injury, Kiryo effects can be brought about there as well.

Kiryo Healing of the Belly of Dogs and Cats: Lying Belly-Up

This is Kiryo healing of the organs; performing Kiryo healing into the nerves of the belly (organs) of a dog or cat that is lying belly-up.

154

Corporal Healing Effects in Dogs and Cats

Corporal healing effects for this process will manifest in much the same way as I have previously described in the "Dogs and Cats: Lying on their Side" section. I believe Kiryo healing effects on the organs (and visceral muscles) are stronger when the pet is lying belly up.

However, there are some pets that are reluctant to expose their belly at all. In the event of such a reluctance, do not force the animal. Kiryo effects will manifest even when the animal is lying on its side: so there is no need to worry.

Kiryo Healing of Other Pets: Birds, Fish, and Others

I have been focusing on describing the methods and effects of Kiryo healing upon dogs and cats, however these methods, as previously mentioned, can work for all types of pets. Other types of pets are also living things, like humans. These pets are also sensitive to the invisible life energy.

155

Kiryo Healing of the Belly *(Internal Organs)* of Dogs and Cats

Kiryo Healing of Birds and Fish

Pets lead their lives relying primarily on their Kiryo nerves. Pets feel and perceive and differentiate the Kiryo life energy sent by the Kiryo practitioners' ku-no-ji palm as healing life-energy. This perception and differentiation allows them to realize that the energy will heal them, and so they relax or slip into a state of Kiryo-sleep. I believe that pets, at some level, know that this energy will bring about Kiryo effects on their illnesses and injuries.

The Kiryo healing between the Kiryo practitioner and their pet is neurotransmissive exchange, which uses the Kiryo practitioner's Kiryo life-energy to heal the pet through vitalization of its nerves. Neurotransmissive exchange is performed through repeated cycles of hand waving and stillness using the five-fingered ku-no-ji palm of the Kiryo practitioner. The most important thing is to *feel as you are* and *be as you are*.

The first pet I performed Kiryo healing on was a parakeet. It had been drooping listlessly on the perch in its cage, but after performing Kiryo healing for about one minute, it began to flap its wings, eat its food, drink water, and look lively.

4. Summary of Kiryo Theory

This chapter is a summary of the core theory of Kiryo, it will be repetitive for many so feel free to skip as necessary.

(1) Revising the Definition of Kiryo

It has taken more than two decades since I was awakened to Kiryo for me to properly establish Kiryo theory (the basic theory). However, as a result, Kiryo has rid itself of the vast, vague concept of "Ki", and has instead solidified a new definition of Kiryo.

The old Kiryo definition was as follows: "Kiryo is the use of Ki energy to heal". According to the currently established Kiryo theory, the definition has been revised to be as follows: "Kiryo is the use of Kiryo life-energy to heal injury and illness and protect against future illness".

The invisible life-energies emitted by our bodies can be divided into two types: natural life-energy and Kiryo life-energy. Our body emits natural life-energy as we live our ordinary life. The source of this natural life-energy is the present (modern) brainstem. Inside this modern brainstem, the primitive brainstem lies dormant. It is this primitive brainstem that is the source of healing life-energy (Kiryo life-energy).

Figure 9: The Relationship between the Wholesome Brainstem and the Cerebral Suppressive Function (A Concept Map of Kiryo Theory)

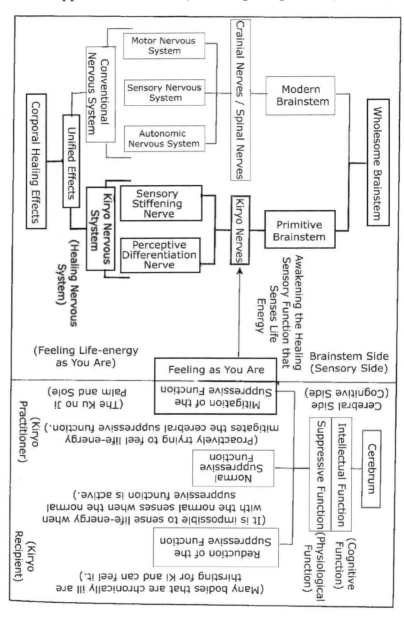

The Kiryo nervous system centered around the primitive brainstem is what draws out and amplifies Kiryo life-energy. The activity of the Kiryo nervous system awakens the healing sensory function that senses life-energy (natural and Kiryo life energies) and affected part energy.

This healing sensory function also simultaneously emits Kiryo life-energy. This Kiryo life-energy can pass through the ku-no-ji palm or sole and stimulate the nerves of another. The exchange, which involves the stimulation of another's nerves using Kiryo life-energy is neurostimulatory exchange; which is neurotransmissive exchange.

Alongside my revision of the definition of Kiryo, I have categorized Ki exchange as neurotransmissive exchange caused by Kiryo life energy.

(2) A Summary of Kiryo Theory

Please look at *Figure 9: The Relationship between the Wholesome Brainstem and the Cerebral Suppressive Function (A Concept Map of Kiryo Theory)*. This chart was drawn up to describe Kiryo theory in a concise, lucid manner. The primary purpose of the chart is to separate daily life and Kiryo (Kiryo exercise & Kiryo healing).

Our daily life is built upon the cerebrum (cognitive side): the normal suppressive function of the cerebrum is active. However, during Kiryo, we depend on the brainstem (sensory side). When performing Kiryo, because of the awareness shift that occurs when attempting to feel life-energy (natural life energy and Kiryo life energy) or affected part energy with the five-fingered ku-no-ji palm, the suppressive function of the cerebrum is mitigated. The same occurs when using the soles of the feet. This mitigated state is the brainstem-mediated (sensory-side) *"feeling as you are"* state, which brings about the neurotransmissive exchange (neurostimulatory exchange) caused by life energy (natural life energy and Kiryo life energy) and affected part energy.

Neurotransmissive exchange awakens the healing sensory function that senses life-energy and affected part energy, and arouses the Kiryo nervous system, which is based around the primitive brainstem.

The main point of Figure 9 is the "two sides of the same coin" relationship that exists between the cerebrum-mediated (cognitive-side)

161

suppressive function and the brainstem-mediated (sensory-side) *feeling as you are*.

When one stops the "feeling as you are" state that occurs in Kiryo, the cerebrum returns to its normal suppressive function, its usual daily state. By the way, during Kiryo, the cognitive activities that allow for creativity and ingenuity are all but unusable. Kiryo is a world of healing sensation, where one *feels as they are*.

Finally, for reference, consider the activity of the autonomic nervous system. The autonomic nervous system is comprised of the sympathetic and parasympathetic nerves. The core of the sympathetic nerves is in the lateral horn of the thoracolumbar region of the spinal cord inside the spine, and is primarily activated during concerted, vigorous movement like, for example, during work or sports. The core of the parasympathetic nervous system is in the brainstem (midbrain, pons, and medulla oblongata) and the sacral spinal cord inside the sacrum, which work during sleep or relaxation.

The central structure of both autonomic nerves—the sympathetic and the parasympathetic nerves—can be found in the hypothalamus of the brainstem (the diencephalon), where it maintains our basic life activities. The hypothalamus controls (dominates) the autonomic nerves.

The cerebral side (cognitive side) is centered around the sympathetic nerve. The parasympathetic system is for the brainstem side (sensory side). From the Kiryo point of view, when Kiryo exercise or Kiryo healing begins, a mitigation of the cerebral suppressive function and the *feel as you are* state causes a switch from sympathetic-centered activity to parasympathetic-centered activity. This is because Kiryo is centered around the wholesome brainstem.

In other words, the mitigation of the cerebral suppressive function and the *feel as you are* state causes, while awake, a switch to parasympathetic-centered activity. It is natural, therefore, for both humans and pets to relax and slip into a Kiryo sleep. Because the parasympathetic nerves become more active, they bring about the wonderful Kiryo effects of recovery on illnesses and injuries. This is because the parasympathetic nerve network is the healing nerve system.

In the world of Kiryo, the *feel as you are* state allows for easy switching between the sympathetic and parasympathetic nerves precisely because it mitigates the cerebral suppressive function. Mitigation of the cerebral

162

suppressive function and the act of *feeling as you are* enables us to have a level of control (dominate) over the sympathetic and parasympathetic nerves.

(3) An Added Supplement to Kiryo Theory

Please look at Figure 10 below, this diagram examines the relationship between the healing sensory function (as suppressed by the cerebrum) and the five senses and helps clarify the existence of the healing sensory function in Kiryo.

Figure 10: The Healing Sensory Function and the Five Senses (Supplementary Diagram)

Cerebral Suppressive Function		Normal Suppressive Function		Mitigated Suppressive Function	
Awareness	Awareness (Psyche)	Passive Awareness		Proactive Awareness	
Environment	Behavioral Environment	Typical Daily Life		Work, Sports, Art, Music, etc.	
Sensation	Nature of the Sensation	Normal Sensation		Sharpened Sensation	
The Five Sensory Functions	Visual Function (eyes)	○	Normal Vision	◎	Proactively Sharpened Vision
	Auditory Function (ears)	○	Normal Audition	◎	Proactively Sharpened Audition
	Olfactory Function (nose)	○	Normal Olfaction	◎	Proactively Sharpened Olfaction
	Gustatory Function (mouth)	○	Normal Gustation	◎	Proactively Sharpened Gustation
	Tactile Function (skin)	○	Normal Tactility	◎	Proactively Sharpened Tactility
The Healing Sensory Function of Kiryo	Placeholder 1	×	Placeholder 2	○	Placeholder 3

164

*Placeholder 1

The Healing Sensory Function (the five-fingered ku-no-ji palm and sole)

*Placeholder 2

Because the healing sensory function is sealed away by the cerebral suppressive function, we cannot sense life energy with the normal senses.

*Placeholder 3

When we proactively attempt to feel life energy, the suppressive function of the cerebrum is mitigated. Our healing sensory function is activated. When we stop attempting to feel, the cerebral suppressive function resumes its normal operation. This applies when we use our soles, too.

When the healing sensory function, which lies latent and dormant within our bodies, is activated, the Kiryo nervous system centered around the primitive brainstem is awakened. The Kiryo nervous system is the nucleus, the centerpoint of Kiryo theory. To supplement the ideas of Kiryo theory, I have juxtaposed the healing sensory function and the five senses.

Thanks to the cerebral suppression function, the normal senses, the five senses, work properly, but the healing sensory function is completely inactive. However, when we work, play sports, do art, or play music, among other things, our proactive awareness causes the suppressive function of the cerebrum to be mitigated. This mitigation enables the five senses to become exceedingly sensitive and precise.

In a similar way, when we attempt to proactively feel life-energy or affected energy with our ku-no-ji palms, we become able to do so. This is because the cerebral suppressive function is mitigated, and the healing sensory function is activated. To put it simply, if we attempt to feel, we can; and if we do not, we cannot. Such is the healing sensory function.

An important point is that once we feel life-energy or affected part energy with our five-fingered ku-no-ji palms, we should simply continue to *feel it as we are*. The same goes for when we feel it with our soles. There is no need for creativity or ingenuity. Simply *feel* and *be as you are*. This is the quintessence of Kiryo.

Chapter 6: A Wholesome (Healthy) Brainstem as a Result of Kiryo

1. Kiryo and Scientific Experimentation: The Television Broadcast

How can we attempt to view Kiryo theory, founded on the principles "Ki exists everywhere", and "Ki is possessed by all", from the perspective of science?

I think there are two paths one can take to prove Kiryo scientifically. The first is to scientifically prove the existence of Ki itself. The second is to scientifically prove the existence of the corporal healing effects (phenomena) generated in the body in response to Ki (Kiryo life energy) exchange. Let's consider these two scientific methodologies.

(1) Proof of the Existence of Ki Through Scientific Experiments

A professor from a university came to visit me one day. After experiencing Kiryo exercise in my classroom, he told me that "it would be an epochal advancement if you managed to physically prove the existence of Ki." In response, I believe it is unlikely at this point in time to scientifically prove the existence of Ki. Although, I do believe a time in which such a proof is possible is just over the horizon.

Even if we cannot prove the existence of Ki scientifically, because Ki exists everywhere, and Ki is shared by everyone, continuing to practice and demonstrate the results of Kiryo will help to prove it. It may also be the purpose of Kiryo to assist in this proof.

(2) Examination of Corporal Healing Effects Through Scientific Experiments

Even if we cannot prove its existence, we can prove the corporal healing effects caused by Ki on the body. The fact that countless animals relaxed, laid down, and fell asleep when exposed to Ki (Kiryo life energy) is one important proof of the existence of Ki.

Another proof is evident by the way that Ki (Kiryo life energy) causes specific corporal healing effects in the human body, effects which can be examined through scientific experimentation. Please look to Figure 11 on page 171, which presents representative data from one such instance of scientific experimentation. This data has been invaluable in scientifically grounding Kiryo theory. This data was kindly made available to me by Yoshio Machi, who was a professor at Tokyo Denki University. This chart examines the results of an experiment in which I used my own body to see whether Ki exists, and what its corporal effects on the body may be.

168

A photo of the author exchanging Ki using the ku-no-ji palm (South Dakota, United States)

A large rhino relaxed, laid down, and fell asleep (Kenya)

From the set-up to the end, let's analyze the scientific Kiryo experiment that was conducted inside a laboratory at Tokyo Denki University.

The Kiryo Life Energy Exchange Experiment between myself (the sender) and the receiver: Mr. A.

1) The two of us sat facing each other about 3 meters apart

2) Electrodes necessary for the gathering of experimental data were affixed to various parts of my body

3) To quiet my body and mind, I rested with eyes closed for approximately 3 minutes

4) Kiryo begins. I exchanged Kiryo life energy for approximately 7 minutes with the receiver (Mr. A)

5) End of Kiryo. The sender, me, rested again with eyes closed for approximately 3 minutes

The experiment proceeded according to steps 1-5 of the procedure outlined above and was over in approximately 13 minutes. Let us now analyze the experimental data.

Figure 11: Kanzawa, Kiryo and Physiological Measurements (focused on blood flow) and their Analysis

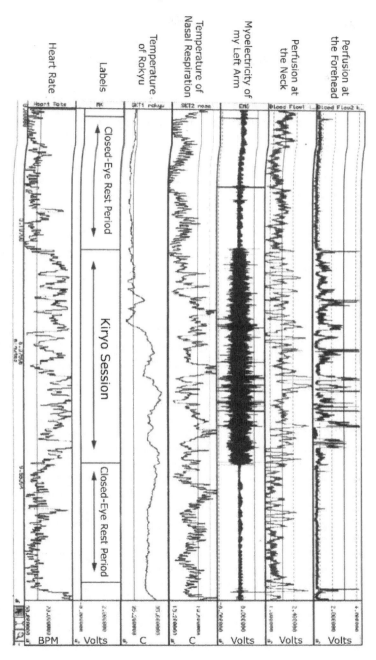

171

First, look at the "marks" row of the figure. You will see the approximately 3-minute-long closed-eye rest I took before beginning Kiryo. This closed-eye rest period was taken in order to cut off stimulatory information from the outside world to my eyes, and to calm the mind and body. We also have the beginning of Kiryo, which was the beginning of the Kiryo life-energy exchange between Mr. A and myself.

I formed my right palm into the ku-no-ji shape and participated in the exchange by sending Ki upwards, downwards, and left and right. I received Mr. A's Ki, and perceived and differentiated that Ki in the form of the hand feedback sensation. The length of the exchange was 7 minutes.

The approximately three-minute-long interval at the end of the Kiryo session was a closed-eye rest period, just like the rest taken at the beginning. This was done for the same reasons: to cut off stimulatory information from the outside world. The entire experiment lasted for about 13 minutes, but its results, as can be seen in the figure, contain several things that are quite valuable for Kiryo.

Look at the waveforms during the meditation before and after the Kiryo session. These waveforms are largely similar. However, the various waveforms—perfusion at the forehead, perfusion at the neck, myoelectricity of my left arm, the temperature of my nasal respiration, the temperature of my Rokyu, and my heart rate— all drastically change during Kiryo (Kiryo life-energy exchange). This change happens right when Kiryo starts, and ends once Kiryo finishes, with the waveforms returning to their normal state.

Myoelectricity refers to the electric potential generated by active muscles, and the Rokyu is the acupuncture point that lies at the center of the depression in the ku-no-ji palm. In other words, this experiment uses electric potential to physiologically measure muscular activity. The chart depicts this data using a waveform. The waveforms during Kiryo are strong and large. They are very steep. However, the waveforms look like gently-sloping mountains before and after Kiryo. What do these steep waveforms and the sudden amplitude changes of the left-arm electromyogram mean?

They show the exchange of Ki (Kiryo life-energy), but also, they show the existence of Ki.

The chart shows that during Kiryo life-energy exchange, the muscles stiffen when one's partner's Ki is felt, and the blood flow, breath, body temperature, and the heart rate all change in response to this. The wholesome brainstem (primitive and modern brainstems) is what controls and sends the strong orders that trigger these changes.

While looking at the "Electromyogram of the Left Arm" row in the figure, let's compare the waveforms before and after Kiryo with the waveforms during Kiryo.

The waveforms during Kiryo are larger and thicker both upwards and downwards.

What does this mean?

The moment I began performing Kiryo, the waveforms began to swing across a much larger vertical area: there amplitude widened. This indicates the muscles are instantaneously undergoing stiffening contractions, and they are relaxing during the recoil from these movements.

During Kiryo life-energy exchange/neurotransmissive exchange, the muscles are continuously undergoing instantaneous stiffening contractions and relaxations (the muscles are stiffening and loosening). The larger and thicker waveforms seen during Kiryo indicate that the muscles have relaxed: they've loosened. During Kiryo, the muscles continuously and regularly undergo instantaneous stiffening contractions. The rebound from these movements cause the muscles to continuously relax and loosen. As a result, the normal muscular contractions and relaxations seen before Kiryo become much larger contractions and relaxations. The larger, thicker waveforms indicate that the contractions and relaxations of the muscles have become more substantial.

Due to this, the muscles are adjusted to become softer, and therefore we refer to the process as *muscular adjustment*. Because the muscles continuously undergo instantaneous stiffening and relaxation, we refer to the phenomenon itself as *continuous* instantaneous *stiffening*. In other words, continuous instantaneous stiffening is muscular adjustment.

Refer to Figure 4, "Diagram of Stiffening Contractions and Relaxations of the Muscles", on page 47. Let's compare Figure 4 and Figure 11.

Do you notice that the extent of muscular contractions and relaxations shown in Figure 4 and the amplitude of the electromyogram of the left arm shown in Figure 11 look similar?

In other words, the pictorial representations of Figure 4 are

173

scientifically explained by the waveform differences in the electromyogram of the left arm seen in Figure 11. Thus, we see that the pictorial representations of muscular stiffening contractions and relaxations are consistent with the experimentally-determined waveforms of the electromyogram of the left arm shown in Figure 11. Another important part of Figure 11 that requires our attention is the fact that the moment I began performing Kiryo, the electromyogram of my left arm, which I was not moving, reacted to this and changed immediately. This is because muscular adjustment caused by instantaneous stiffening began. The waveforms in each column all simultaneously and instantaneously changed to become bigger.

What does this simultaneous waveform change mean? It means that all the muscles in my body—skeletal and visceral muscles, etc.—underwent muscular adjustment, caused by continued instantaneous stiffening. The moment I began the Kiryo life-energy exchange, I received Mr. A's Ki (natural life energy) in my right ku-no-ji palm, and instantaneous stiffening contractions and relaxations occurred in all the muscles of my body, not just those of my right arm. The moment my right ku-no-ji palm sent Ki to Mr. A and received Mr. A's Ki (natural life-energy), every muscle in my body underwent continued instantaneous stiffening. The muscles in all parts of my body were adjusted.

As proof that all muscles in my body were adjusted, the blood flow amount (perfusion) in my forehead and neck, the temperature of my nasal respiration, the temperature of my Rokyu, and my heart rate are all displayed. Conversely, if muscular adjustment had not occurred, none of these simultaneous, continued changes would have occurred.

This proves that sensory stiffening nerves exist in every part of my body. The activity of these sensory stiffening nerves is what caused all the muscles of my body to be adjusted. This whole-body muscular adjustment caused my blood flow, respiration, body temperature, and heart rate to together become more vigorous all at the same time.

I remember a certain incident when thinking of all this: my Asahi Television program in Kenya, where I exchanged Ki with a rhinoceros.

The moment I began Ki exchange with the rhinoceros, my right palm changed from a ku-no-ji shape into a fist. Because the life-energy of the rhinoceros was so strong, my right palm instantaneously underwent stiffening contractions and formed into a fist. If, at that time, there were electrodes placed all over my body and I was taking part in a scientific experiment, I am

174

sure that the electromyogram waves being measured would have swung large and thick.

(3) Correlations Between Figure 11 and Figure 7

Let's compare the scientific experimental data of Figure 11, on page 171, and Figure 7, "Diagram of the Relationship between the Three Healing Adjustments", on page 58.

Look at Figure 11, "Kanzawa; Kiryo and Physiological Measurements". The "forehead perfusion" and "neck perfusion" portions of the figure are instances of blood flow adjustment. "Electromyogram of the Left Arm" is an instance of muscular adjustment. The "Nasal Respiration Temperature" portion of the figure is an instance of external respiration changing after coupling with internal respiration (cellular respiration), and is therefore an instance of breath (respiratory) adjustment.

Following that line of thinking, I believe one should be able to see that the three adjustments shown in Figure 7, "Diagram of the Relationship between the Three Healing Adjustments", on Page 97—muscular adjustment, blood flow adjustment, and respiratory adjustment (the three adjustments principle)—align with the data shown on Figure 11.

In other words, the three adjustments principle (the three healing adjustments) was proven by a scientific experiment using my body. I will omit a detailed explanation of the three adjustments principle—please reread the chapter on the three healing adjustments if needed.

As a result, blood flow adjustment brings about immune adjustment, hormonal adjustment, and temperature adjustment, among other things. With regards to immune adjustment and hormonal adjustment, we ought to see a change in immune and hormonal levels if we do a blood test. Of course, changes in body temperature and the like can be easily noticed with the proper measurements. Mental adjustment occurs easily if bodily adjustment can occur.

While Ki itself (Kiryo life energy) remains unproven, we now know that the corporal healing effects manifested upon the human body by Ki can easily be proven using modern medical technology.

2. A Wholesome Brainstem as an Effect of Kiryo

(1) The Effects of Kiryo Partner-Healing

Kiryo partner-healing is using neurotransmissive exchange to recover and restore the illnesses and injuries of a Kiryo recipient.

While performing Kiryo healing, I am often asked "How many times will I have to do this before I get better?"

I believe this depends on seven conditions, so I answer, "It depends. I cannot say how many." These conditions apply even for the same illness, as different people respond differently to Kiryo. So, here are the seven conditions:

1. **Age:** The young and the old have differing life forces and immune system strength, and therefore can have differing rates of recovery and restoration

2. **Sex:** Men and Women are physiologically different, and therefore can have differing rates of recovery and restoration

3. **Genetic Makeup:** The genetics of both mother and father define the genetic makeup, and they differ greatly person to person. This can cause differing rates of recovery and restoration

4. **Symptoms:** Illnesses and injuries vary in their severity (from mild, to moderate, to life-threatening); this can cause differing rates of recovery and restoration

5. **Duration:** Differences in the amount of time since the first emergence of symptoms and the time that one seeks treatment can cause differing rates of recovery and restoration

6. **Other Ailments:** Whether or not the patient has one or more other ailments can cause differing rates of recovery and restoration

7. **Health level:** Differences in the physical and mental wellbeing of an individual can cause differing rates of recovery and restoration

176

These seven conditions, together, apply to cause differences in the rates of recovery and restoration of even two people that suffer from an identical injury or illness. Kiryo involves the use of the Kiryo practitioner's healing power to carry out both the three healing adjustments and the healing adjustment of mind and body. In doing so, it assists greatly in the treatment of injury and illness. This is the essence of Kiryo partner-healing.

The following are three unforgettable examples of Kiryo healings that I personally witnessed.

Case A: *Herniated Lumbar Disc* (Male, 35 years old)

A man came to receive Kiryo healing from me the day before he was scheduled to be admitted for surgery on his herniated lumbar disc. Sensation to his legs was almost completely numbed; I placed a cold orange against his thigh, and he could not feel it.

I was just an amateur, and did not fully understand even the basics of Kiryo healing. I asked him to lie on his stomach, and I waved my right palm back and forth about four inches above his waist.

I continued hand-waving with my *ku no ji* palm for about 20 minutes. Afterwards, I asked him how his back felt. He was sitting cross-legged when the sensation returned to his legs. He placed the cold orange against his thigh again, and he could feel it.

He then placed his ankles on the low table in front of him and began to do sit-ups. He, his companion, and I were all amazed that he could do such a thing.

He ended up not needing his surgery. His herniated lumbar disc had recovered and restored itself.

Case B: *Fibromyalgia* (Female, 52 years old)

A woman had been bedridden for 16 years due to fibromyalgia. The mats underneath her bed had been replaced twice after being soaked through with

177

her sweat. Her pain was so severe that even the smallest of things, like a person passing through the room, or the wind blowing through the window, would cause her great discomfort.

This was a case I took during my amateur years, right after I realized that the soles of the feet also possess the ability to heal.

I placed the sole of my right foot approximately four inches away from the patient's own feet as she lay face up in her bed. I began neurotransmissive exchange between the soles of our feet. After about five minutes, both of the patient's knees began to slightly move up and down in turns. Eventually, they began to move both up and down and side to side rather dramatically.

Today, I call these reactions body-external (actualized) stiffening phenomena caused by muscular adjustment brought about by sustained instantaneous stiffening. They are a corporal healing effect.

At the time, I had never seen someone's body move in response to Kiryo healing performed with the feet. After five sessions of Kiryo healing, the patient's pain from her fibromyalgia subsided considerably, and about half a year later, her health was recovered and restored.

Case C: *Hepatitis C and Hepatic Cancer* (Female, 50 years old)

As a result of hepatitis C, a woman had developed cirrhosis, followed by hepatic cancer. She was given about 3 months to live. She received Kiryo healing from me twice. Three months later, she reached out to me again.

Apparently, while her hepatitis C remained, her cirrhosis and hepatic cancer had completely recovered and restored themselves. Just to be sure, she had apparently had herself tested three separate times.

One may wonder how Kiryo effects caused such miraculous recovery and restoration. I will explain by detailing their instances through the lens of Kiryo theory.

In the case of the herniated lumbar disc, I believe sustained instantaneous stiffening adjusted the lower back muscles and softened them causing these muscles to regain their normal strength and once again become able to support the waist, and finally placed the herniated lumbar disc back in the right place. This all happened within 20 minutes.

178

Next is the case of the woman with hepatitis C, cirrhosis, and hepatic cancer. I suppose that the neurotransmissive exchange of Kiryo life-energy awakened her Kiryo nerves, activated her primeval life functions—such as the primitive brainstem and the ancient immune system—which then brought about her recovery.

The primeval life functions are activated when illness or injury threaten one's life, and manifest strong Kiryo effects when stimulated by the neurotransmissive exchange seen in Kiryo healing.

Cases in which the Wholesome Brainstem Has Manifested Kiryo Effects (Recovery and Restoration)

The following is a list of the names of disorders Kiryo practitioners, students, and myself have performed Kiryo healing on.

➤   *Brain and Nervous System Disorders*

Headache, migraine, autonomic dysfunction, psychophysiological disorder, neurotic disorder, depression, panic attack, depersonalization syndrome, stroke, brain infarct, hemorrhage, Parkinson's disease, trigeminal neuralgia, facial paralysis, dementia, brain tumor, cerebral aneurysm, general malaise, facial spasm, and cerebral arteriosclerosis.

➤   *Muscular and skeletal disorders*

Shoulder stiffness, frozen shoulder, whiplashes, tenosynovitis, low back pain, cranioplasia, lumber vertebrae herniated disk, sciatica, numbness of the arms, arthralgia, sprains, bone fractures, bruise disorders, knee arthritis, deformed knee arthritis, hip arthritis, hip dislocation, subluxation, ganglion, jammed finger, muscle pain, muscle contusion, achillodynia, cut, burn, rheumatoid arthritis, muscle rheumatism, myofascial pain, atopic dermatitis, sports injury, etc.

179

➢ Circulatory system disorders (heart, blood vessel, lymphatic vessel)

Angina pectoris, cardiac infarction, myocardial inflammation, irregular pulse, palpitations, arteriosclerosis, high blood pressure, hypotension, Atrial fibrillation, Ventricular fibrillation, Cardiac hypertrophy, cardiectasia, aneurysm, Varicose veins, poor circulation, circulation defect, Raynaud's disease, and Anemia

➢ *Respiratory system disorders* (organ, bronchial tube, lung)

Tracheitis, bronchitis, bronchial asthma, bronchiectasis, pneumonia, interstitial pneumonia, emphysema, hyperventilation syndrome, and sleep apnea syndrome

➢ Digestive system disorders (oral cavity, esophagus, stomach, duodenum, small intestine, large intestine, liver, pancreas)

Stomatitis, reflux esophagitis, esophagus achalasia, gastritis, gastroptosia, gastric dilation, gastric ulcer, gastric polyp, duodenal ulcer, acute enteritis, irritable bowel syndrome, constipation, diarrhea, ulcerative colitis, colon polyp, intestinal obstruction, hemorrhoids, anorexia, hepatitis, cirrhosis, fatty liver syndrome, alcoholic liver injury, cholelithiasis pancreatitis, diabetes, and complications from diabetes

➢ *Urinary system disorders* (kidney, ureter, bladder)

Nephritis, kidney failure, kidney stone, ureteral stone, cystitis, pollakiuria, enuresis, urethritis, benign prostatic hyperplasia, incontinence, complications of kidney disease, and uremia

➤ *Gynecological Disorders*

Menstrual irregularity, menstrual pain, amenorrhea, discomfort caused by pregnancy, uterine myoma, endometriosis, and ovarian cysts

➤ *Organs in the head* (eyes, ears, nose, throat)

Asthenopia, itchy eye, pink eye, dry eye, watery eye, cataract, glaucoma, keratoconus, macular degeneration

tympanitis, external otitis, ear noise, auditory hallucination, Ménierè disease, rhinitis, allergic rhinitis, empyema, deviation of the nasal septum, tonsilitis, overactive thyroid, and hypothyroidism

➤ *Cancer*

Esophageal cancer, gastric cancer, lung cancer, breast cancer, Hodgkin's disease, colorectal cancer, liver cancer, hepatic carcinoma, pancreatic cancer, bladder cancer, bone cancer, etc.

➤ *Other symptoms with pains from unknown causes*

Please Note:

Kiryo functions as a supplement to modern medicine with its focus on Kiryo healing and Kiryo exercise. Its purpose is to assist in the recovery and restoration of illness and injury alongside the guidance of a medical professional. Kiryo is not a replacement for modern medicine. In addition, it is also Kiryo's purpose to cause health promotion, which can help prevent disease.

(2) The Effects of Kiryo Healing on Pets

The human primeval life functions have been forced into a latent slumber due to the development of the cerebrum. However, animals, especially wild animals, have lived since ancient times with their primeval life functions intact. Let us now consider these primeval life functions. The primeval life functions include the primitive brainstem and the ancient immune system.

The primitive brainstem presides over the Kiryo nervous system (Kiryo nerve, perceptive differentiation nerve, sensory stiffening nerve) and the autonomic nerves. The ancient immune system also remains, to some extent, in the human body, and in times of emergency, it activates. This ancient immune system is a primeval immune system that comes into effect when one's life is in danger.

Wild animals, to survive the harsh natural conditions in which they live, possess a healing power rooted in the primitive brainstem and the ancient immune system: they possess a strong self-healing power. I also believe that animals possess the ability to heal others. I would like to examine this power to heal others.

When I perform Kiryo healing on animals, most of them relax and fall asleep. Demonstrated examples of this include two hundred buffalos in Kenya and two hundred bison in the United States.

Why was it that most of these animals went unconscious under the effect of Kiryo?

I believe the answer to that question can be found by examining Kiryo partner-healing.

Wild animals live while emitting their strong life-energy. They also sense the life-energy emitted by other animals during their daily lives.

The perceptive/differentiative ability of animals lies in a world of sensation far beyond what humans can imagine. For instance, a dog's olfactory sense is approximately 3,000 times more powerful than that of a human.

So, what does that mean for buffalo and bison?

182

Both the buffalo and bison emit strong life-energy. As a result of primeval life function, they perceive and differentiate each other's life energy while gathering in a herd, and so live out their lives. When I used partner-healing power and begin Kiryo healing (neurotransmissive exchange), both the buffalo and the bison acutely perceived and differentiated this energy (perceptive differentiation nerve).

At the same time, muscular adjustment brought about by sustained instantaneous stiffening (sensory stiffening nerve) occurs, as does blood flow adjustment and respiratory adjustment: the three adjustments principle comes into effect. The activation of this, causes both the life energies and the life energy perceptive/differentiative abilities of the buffalo and bison to heighten. Within both the buffalo and bison herds, the heightening of life-energy and life-energy perceptive/differentiative ability were synergistically amplified, eventually forming an accumulated energy that transformed the space around these animals into a healing Kiryo Space.

Inside this Kiryo space, the buffalo and bison relaxed, contentedly, laid down, and eventually slipped into a Kiryo sleep or a Kiryo sleep-like state. The energy in this Kiryo sleep state is several times stronger than that which is felt while awake. This applies to humans in Kiryo sleep as well.

During Kiryo healing, the Kiryo recipient's life-energy significantly changes. The hand feedback sensation felt in the ku-no-ji palm allows for perception and differentiation of the change in the life-energy of the Kiryo recipient. In fact, the recipient themselves falls into Kiryo sleep through this perception and differentiation.

I believe a normal bison continually exchanges strong life-energy (self- and other-healing power) throughout its life. Into this mix, I added my Kiryo life-energy by beginning Kiryo healing (neurotransmissive exchange). Upon doing so, the three adjustments principle was activated in the bison, and then they relaxed and began to lay down one after another, eventually slipping into Kiryo sleep.

I performed this, for the first time, on approximately 100 bison. Right in the middle of this Kiryo healing, many more came pouring down the slope of a hill in the distance like an approaching summer rain. There were then about twice as many as when I had started healing. Still, these bison that gathered also began to lay down, one by one, and slipped into Kiryo sleep. A silent, peaceful healing Kiryo space was born under the early morning sun.

Why, in the middle of my Kiryo healing, did the second group of 100 bison gather and then slip into Kiryo sleep?

They perceived and differentiated the healing Kiryo space created by the first 100 bison, entered it, and thus were put to sleep. What attracted the bison to the Kiryo space?

The truth is that Kiryo sleep is a powerful healing sleep. The Kiryo space is pervaded by strong life-energy and is a space of healing Kiryo sleep. In other words, the Kiryo space was one where the self- and other-healing powers were especially strong.

The bison that arrived afterwards gathered in search of the healing power of the Kiryo space, expanded that Kiryo space, and then slipped into Kiryo sleep. This Kiryo sleep caused their life energy to heighten and gather, eventually forming an accumulated energy that created the Kiryo space. Put another way, the accumulated energy created the healing Kiryo space that magnified the self- and other-healing powers.

Thus, we can conclude that the bison that came afterwards entered a Kiryo space permeated by a strong healing power. As a result, the 100-bison Kiryo-space became a Kiryo space with the accumulated energy of 200-bison.

In truth, it was not my Kiryo healing power that caused most of the bison to enter Kiryo sleep. The reason the bison entered into Kiryo sleep is because an exchange occurred between the life-energy known as other-healing power (partner healing power) and the self-healing power that these bison themselves possessed. This exchange gave rise to a Kiryo space (symbiotic healing power space). The role of my Kiryo healing was to ignite the process by initially creating the Kiryo space, and to heighten and amplify the accumulated energy of the Kiryo space.

For reference, let us consider the relationship between animals and Kiryo. I would surmise that animals do not respond to cerebral brain waves, but they do respond and can act in concord to brainstem waves—more accurately, the waves of the primitive brainstem.

The Primeval Life Functions Humans Have Forgotten

Humans have come to forget their primeval life functions. This is because the primeval life functions are sealed by the normal, suppressive activity of the cerebrum.

The Source of the Self-Healing and Partner-Healing Powers are the Primeval Life Functions

The primeval life functions that are the source of the self- and partner healing powers are possessed, albeit latently, by all. These life functions can be actualized by awakening through *feeling as you are*, because the Kiryo nervous system is centered around the primitive brainstem. As for specific methods, Kiryo exercise and Kiryo healing enable one to awaken and heighten these functions.

My Brainstem Shocks Were the Awakening of my Primeval Life Functions

The brainstem shocks were the awakening of my primitive brainstem and ancient immune system: my primeval life functions. My awakened primeval life functions made short work of many of my illnesses.

Why were these illnesses swept away, and why was I able to master the self- and partner-healing powers?

I worried for many years over this mystifying fact. Yet, the establishment of Kiryo Theory has elucidated and lifted away this worry.

Afterword

In Kiryo, I have kept the ideas of Ki existing everywhere, of being shared by all humans, and of being body-external—the idea becoming a medium for natural energy—as basic elements of the discipline. However, despite frequently using the terms "Ki" and "Ki energy", explaining these concepts concretely proved difficult, and I racked my brains for many years trying to overcome this obstacle.

At the end of the day, the root of the problem lies in the fact that there exist no commonly-used words in Japanese that can describe a Ki used to heal illness and injury. What I mean by this is there are phrases in Japanese like, "*Genki de!*" ("Be well!) or "*Ki wo tsukete!*" ("Take care!") that are used in a variety of situations, but even though we have known of illnesses and injuries being healed by an invisible energy, we have never had words to explain this phenomenon. As a result, we have only been able to process this concept by resorting to feelings of awe or mysterious wonder, or even labeling them as superhuman or special powers.

Verbalizing the phenomenon by which injuries and illnesses are healed by an invisible energy was heretofore impossible. This is because, in my sphere of thought, there was no trace of even the idea of illnesses and injuries being healed through Ki... and that same problem persists for many even today. In addition to the lack of vocabulary to detail the healing of illness and injury with Ki, the suppressive activity of the cerebrum has sealed the healing sensory function triggered by the activity of the Kiryo nervous system. This was also one of the reasons why I was unable to approach the idea of Ki, and why I was incapable of understanding it.

Just as the cerebrum restricts us from sensing life-energy, it has suppressed and sealed off the activity of the Kiryo nervous system centered around the primitive brainstem. It is thought that this suppressive function was necessary in order to jumpstart human cognitive function, and enable

186

the performing of cognitive activities, such as language.

When Kiryo exercise and Kiryo healing begin through *feeling as one is*, the suppressive function of the cerebrum is mitigated, and within the body, Kiryo life-energy, which heals illness and injury, is produced. In other words, this Kiryo life-energy is nothing but the symbiotic life force that lies sleeping inside our bodies.

The impetus that spurred me twenty-five years ago into the world of Kiryo was the brainstem and bodily shocks—which occurred as I was fast asleep, in the dead of night—that awakened my Kiryo nervous system. I believe that while I was asleep, the suppressive function of my cerebrum was mitigated, and while it was mitigated, some physiological function that awakened the activity of my Kiryo nervous system was activated.

Inside our bodies there exists an internal healing force—a natural healing power—that heals our illnesses and injuries. In this modern age, thanks to the findings of chemists, doctors, and nutritionists, we strive to heighten this natural healing power using various special foods, supplements, and herbal teas—among other things.

There is a strong general awareness of health and healthiness, and creativity and ingenuity to maintain this healthiness have become commonplace in our society.

I, too, after being recommended it by others, have come to enjoy drinking Jason Winters Tea (JWT) herbal teas. After starting to drink herbal teas, there have been times where I have felt an increase in my natural healing power. Before this whenever I would brush my teeth, my unstable gums would bleed. In fact, two of my back teeth were wobbly, and when biting food, they would especially hurt. After approximately two months of drinking herbal tea, I noticed that my gums had become more stable, and that the two bothersome back teeth no longer hurt when eating. This was quite surprising, and I was naturally grateful.

In addition to this, I was practicing Kiryo as part of my job, and my symbiotic healing power was strong, and I was healthy, but I felt like my cells were even further vitalized, and there was a vigor energizing my whole body. I suppose you might call this a collaboration of my natural healing power and symbiotic healing power.

If we liken one's internal healing ability to the moon, then from a phenomenological, Kiryo perspective, the bright, shining half of the moon

187

is our natural healing power, and the dark half of the moon is our symbiotic healing power.

Nowadays, we tend to think of the half-moon of the natural healing power as the end-all and be-all. Yet, we should also unearth the symbiotic healing power, a new discovery made through Kiryo, and make use of it as well.

The use of the symbiotic healing power will turn a dark half-moon into a brightly-lit one. When the bright half-moon of the natural healing power and the bright half-moon of the symbiotic healing power come together, they form the ideal full moon.

This bright full moon, symbolic of the internal healing force, will proactively treat illness and injury, protect against future illness, and assist us in being healthy.

Thanks to the establishment of the Kiryo theory laid out in this book, from now on, Kiryo will take the following ideas as its foundation:

In Kiryo, the symbiotic healing power will be considered internal: a power possessed by all. And Kiryo itself the process of unifying oneself with natural energy.

Now, I have just one final statement to make. If one were to liken healing power to a flower, then alongside the currently blooming flower of natural healing power, let us also bloom the other flower, the sleeping source of health itself, the symbiotic healing power! Allow this to open and show its glory to the world!

I strongly hope that Kiryo will continue to spread, and that, in doing so, it will continue to assist people in promoting their own health and the health of others.

Health Promotion Act
(Promulgated August 2, Heisei 14 (2002))

(Included for reference)

Article 1

(Objective)

This law seeks to, in accordance with the rapid progression of societal aging and the changing nature of illness and disease in our country, and in light of the significantly growing importance of the health of the people, through the establishment of basic facts with regards to the implementation of a comprehensive promotion of popular health and the laying out of measures to target the health promotion of the populace, including, but not limited to, nutritional reform, aim for the improvement of national health.

Article 2

(The Duty of the People)

The people must deepen their understanding and interest in the importance of healthy habits, and, throughout their lives, both be aware of the state of their health and strive towards its improvement.

Article 3

(The Duty of the Nation and Regional Public Organizations)

The country and regional public organizations must strive to aim for the dissemination of accurate knowledge pertinent to health promotion through education and public relations, the collection, organization, analysis, and provision and implementation of research into and the training and improvement of the quality of individuals involved in health promotion, and the supply of necessary technological support to all those involved in health promotion project implementation and related endeavors.

Glossary

- Composed Pulse (ゆったり打ち)

    - The proof of good blood circulation. A composed pulse is the manifestation of blood flow adjustment and signifies good blood circulation.

- Corporal Healing Effect (癒しの体現作用)

    - A specific healing effect visible in the body as a result of an adjustment or exercise.

- Healing Sensory Function: (癒しの感覚機能)

    - The ability to sense Ki energy (life and healing life energies).

- Hand Feedback Sensation (手応感覚)

    - The various sensations felt in the palm in response to Ki. These are a product of the interaction between Ki and the nervous system. Perceiving and differentiating these sensations is the task of the perceptive differentiation nerve.

- Healing Adjustment of Mind and Body (癒しの心身調整)

    - A comprehensive term referring to all the specific physiological adjustments made to the body by Kiryo.

- Instantaneous Stiffening Contraction (瞬間的硬直収縮)

    - The stiffening process mediated by the sensory stiffening nerve that causes muscular adjustment in Kiryo, thereby leading to a variety of different healing effects.

- Internal Respiration (Cellular Respiration) (体内呼吸)

- During respiration, glucose and oxygen react, carbon dioxide is produced, and energy is released as a byproduct. This is the oxygen and carbon dioxide gas exchange process; it is also referred to as internal respiration or cellular respiration. Because internal respiration is carried out at the level of each individual cell, in Kiryo, it gained the name cellular respiration.

- Ki (気)

  - A pervasive, omnipresent natural energy that Kiryo practitioners become a medium for during Kiryo by feeling as they are. Ki is life force and symbiotic life force. Drawing out and heightening Ki energy is a definite method of achieving health promotion. Kiryo theory holds that Ki cannot be controlled or manipulated through creative, ingenious, proactive thought. One can only surrender oneself to Ki and allow oneself to become a conduit for this energy.

- Ki Response Sensation (気応感覚)

  - A comprehensive term referring to the feedback sensations felt in all parts of the body in response to Ki energy.

- Kiryo (気療)

  - Recovery from illness or injury. In other words, it means the process by which the internal body heals and recovers from sickness or damage. The Kiryo practitioner's healing power performs the Three Healing Adjustments and adjusts the healing of both one's mind and body; this helps to recover a wound or a sickness.

- Kiryo Nerves (気療神経)

  - A comprehensive term referring to the nerves held to exist under Kiryo theory: the sensory stiffening nerve and the perception differentiating nerve.

191

- Kiryo Space (気療空間)

  - An area suffused with Ki energy through the practice of Kiryo. From the text: "Within both the buffalo and bison herds, the heightening of life energy and life energy perceptive/differentiative ability were synergistically amplified, eventually forming an accumulated energy that transformed the space around these animals into a healing Kiryo Space (other-person healing power space)."

- Kiryo Practitioner (気療者)

  - The individual administering Kiryo during a treatment, or anyone practicing Kiryo exercise. An active participant in Ki exchange.

- Kiryo Recipient (被気療者)

  - Anyone that receives Kiryo treatment or Ki energy from a Kiryo practitioner.

- Ku-no-ji Palm (くの字)

  - Literally meaning "the ku character." The ku character is this: く. The shape into which one should form their hand and palm when performing Kiryo. Bend one's fingers forward at the outermost knuckles and form the hand into a shape like the ku character, as if catching water in the palm of one's hand. The ku no ji palm is also known as "the ancient palm." It is believed that before improved cerebral function, the ancients were less dexterous with their fingers, so the "ku" form was natural.

- Modern Brainstem (現在の脳幹)

  - The current state of the brainstem, following years of suppression and sealing by the continuously-evolving cerebrum. It is weak, incapable of addressing its original function: defense of the body from threats.

192

- Neurotransmissive Exchange (神経伝達交流)

    - Literally meaning, "nerve-transmission-exchange." The exchange of Ki energy that stimulates the nervous systems of all who participate. (Further clarification by translator at end of glossary).

- Other-Person Healing Ability (他者治癒力)

    - The ability to use Ki energy to heal other people. Kiryo uses the Kiryo practitioner's healing power to perform the Three Healing Adjustments and adjust the healing of both the mind and body of the patient; this helps to recover a wound or a sickness.

- Primeval Life Function (原始の生命機能)

    - The ancient functions of the brainstem that keep our body alive. The combination of the ancient immune system and primitive brainstem.

- Perceptive Differentiation Nerve (感知判別神経)

    - More directly it is the perceiving and discriminating nerve. This nerve is responsible for sensing Ki energy as well as differentiating energy variations. All of us have this nerve, it merely lies dormant within us.

- Primitive Brainstem (太古の脳幹)

    - The ancient brainstem that resides dormant in our modern, current brainstems. It is responsible for allowing us to feel Ki response sensations and participate in Ki exchange. It can only be awakened from its slumber by ridding oneself of cognitive activity —the process of "feeling as you are."

- Primitive Cerebrum (太古の大脳)

    - The pre-evolutionary state of the cerebrum. It was incapable of complex cognition/language and was largely

193

subservient to the primitive brainstem.

- Symbiotic Healing Power (自他治癒力)

    - A comprehensive term referring to both types of healing: healing of oneself, and healing of others. Kiryo exercise leads to improvement of the symbiotic healing power.

- Sensory Stiffening Nerve (感覚硬直神経)

    - The nerve responsible for causing instantaneous stiffening and relaxation to the muscles in response to the detection of Ki energy. This makes the hand, or other part of the body, appear and feel rigid. This is the primary healing function and the beginning of the three healing adjustments.

- Three Adjustments Principle (三調整の原理)

    - The collective name for the three adjustments caused by Kiryo that effect healing in the body: muscular adjustment, blood flow adjustment, and respiratory adjustment.

- Wholesome Brainstem (健全な脳幹)

    - The awakened primitive brainstem unifies with the modern brainstem to create the wholesome brainstem. This wholesome brainstem sends powerful orders to keep living to the Kiryo and modern medical nervous systems. Directly translated as "Healthy Brainstem."

Clarifications from the Translator Regarding "Neurotransmissive Exchange"

The term "neuro-transmissive exchange" is, in Japanese, 神経伝達交流. It is literally "nerve-transmission-exchange." For example, the exchange of invisible healing life-energy from one body to another.

Well, "neuro-" actually is just the prefix form of nerve. Diseases of the nerves are called "neuropathies," like "diabetic neuropathy." 神経 in

194

Japanese is commonly translated as "neuro-" when it is inside a compound word. 神経科学 is "neuroscience," 神経科 is "neurology" or "neurologist," etc. 神経伝達物質 ("nerve-transmission-substance") is "neurotransmitter." (this is where I got the idea of translating the term as neurotransmissive exchange).

From a biological perspective, the brain is actually considered part of the nervous system. That's why we commonly associate "neuro-" with the brain. Lastly, in Kiryo theory, the brain is actually part of the Kiryo nervous system. The brainstem is constantly referred to as the cornerstone, etc., of Kiryo itself. And neurotransmissive exchange as described by Kanzawa does indeed involve both the nerves (of the palm, etc.) and the brain as well.

Author Timeline

Tadashi Kanzawa

January 1944	Born in Gunma Prefecture.
March 1968	Graduates from the Department of Law at Meiji University.
December 1971	Begins work as a civil servant.
January 1988	Strange things happen to his body. From January to March, brainstem shocks happen a total of six times, all during the middle of the night, while asleep. Because of this, he is awakened to the power of Ki (self-healing power), heals several of his own illnesses, and realizes that this is effective against the illnesses and injuries of another as well. Since then, he has healed tens of thousands of people.
March 1992	Quits his civil service position and goes to Tokyo.
April 1992	Devotes himself to the research and practice of the power of Ki and begins to spread word about the power of Ki.
July 1994	Stays for one month in Avignon, France, to spread word about the power of Ki.
February 1995	Publishes *Kiryo* (Tamade Publishers).
May 1996	Publishes *Remote Kiryo* (Tamade Publishers)
August	Founds the Kiryo School.

1996	
November 1997	Appears on TBS Television's "Bizarre Animals!"
June 1998	Appears on Fuji Television's "Miraculous Experiences! Unbelievable!"
August 1998	Opens the Kiryo Academy (renames the "Kiryo School")
July 1999	Opens the Paris branch of the Kiryo Academy.
April 2001	Appears on Asahi Televison's "For Real?! Australia Edition."
October 2001	Appears on Asahi Television's "For Real?! Spain Edition."
December 2001	Appears on Asahi Television's "For Real?! Kenya Edition."
June 2002	Appears on Korea TV's Japan-Korea World Cup Commemorative Special Program.
October 2002	Appears on Asahi Television's "For Real?! Siberia Edition."
December 2002	Starts a model business for the dispatch of Kiryo practitioners.
February 2004	Publishes *Healing with Kiryo* (Tamade Publishers)
June 2005	Appears on Asahi's "Global Supernatural Occurrences Council (America Edition)."
January 2006	Opens the Osaka branch of the Kiryo Academy.
February 2006	Appears on Korea Television's KBS.
April 2006	Appears on Japan Television's "Special

	Mission Research 200X."
July 2006	Appears on TBS Television's "Bizarre Animals!"
February 2007	Establishes the Remote Kiryo Network.
November 2007	Appears on Fuji Television's "Supernatural Academy 2007."
May 2013	Publishes *Study of Kiryo: Awaken the Symbiotic Healing Power.*

About the Translator

Nimish K. Pratha graduated with Latin honors from the University of California, San Diego with degrees in Biology and Linguistics. He has taken research-intensive, college-level courses in genetics, molecular biology, physiology, neurobiology, metabolic biochemistry and organic chemistry, and was a USA Biology Olympiad finalist. Nimish also has significant research experience in myriad areas of biology, including cellular signaling, endobiogeny, and bioinformatics. As the son of a gastroenterologist, he was raised around medicine and volunteered at his mother's clinic throughout high school. Nimish has also worked as a translator and interpreter of Japanese for over three years, and recently published a corpus analysis of the content and presentation of sound effects in American comics and Japanese manga. He is deeply interested in neuroscience, language, and how the two interact.

Books of Similar Interest

Healing with Kiryo: The Adventures and Teachings of Tadashi Kanzawa – Tadashi Kanzawa

Enter Mo Pai: The Ancient Training of the Immortals – James Van Gelder

Enter the Infinite – James Van Gelder

Wheel of Knowledge Publishing

www.WheelofKnowledge.org

84103869R00122

Made in the USA
San Bernardino, CA
03 August 2018